New Leaves

ECONOMY READING SERIES

Louise Matteoni
Floyd Sucher
Marvin Klein
Karen Welch

THE ECONOMY COMPANY

Oklahoma City
Indianapolis
Los Angeles

Cover Illustration: Mike Wimmer

Permission to use or adapt copyrighted material appearing
in this book is gratefully acknowledged on pages 331-332,
which are hereby made a part of this copyright page.

ISBN 0-8332-2584-7

THE ECONOMY COMPANY, Educational Publishers
1200 Northwest 63rd Street
Oklahoma City, Oklahoma 73116-5712

5 6 7 8 9 10 — 90 89 88 87

Contents

Chances

Words to Know for First Aid

Experiences

Muscles at Work

When I Read

Words to Know for Computers

Wishes

Flat Stanley

a story by Jeff Brown

How I Got My Ten-Speed Bike

Footprints

Mysteries

Promises

Cunningham's Rooster

Benny's Flag

Journeys

CHANCES

What's the Matter with Carruthers?

New Words

1. He has an <u>unpleasant</u> look on his face.
2. I <u>plopped</u> down in the chair beside him.
3. <u>Emily</u> is very cheerful.
4. He is being <u>grumpy</u> today.
5. "Oh, no!" she <u>exclaimed</u>.
6. We went for a <u>stroll</u> through the park.
7. My friend <u>Carruthers</u> is seven years old.
8. My mom kept us <u>busy</u> all day long.
9. He and I <u>both</u> like to play baseball.
10. They invited me to lunch, so of <u>course</u> I went.

What's the Matter with Carruthers?

James Marshall

One fall morning Emily Pig and her friend Eugene were enjoying a stroll in the park.

"What beautiful weather," said Emily. "I'm sure we are going to meet some of our friends here today."

"That would be very nice," said Eugene.

Sure enough, they came upon their old friend Carruthers sitting alone on a wooden bench, busy staring at the falling leaves.

"Good morning, Carruthers," they both called out in their most cheerful voices.

"Good morning," said Carruthers. But his voice was far from cheerful. It was the kind of "good morning" that really means, "Go away, I want to be left alone."

"I'm worried about Carruthers," Emily whispered to Eugene. "He hasn't been himself lately. He's so grumpy and unpleasant."

"It's not like Carruthers to be unpleasant," Eugene whispered back. "He always has a kind word for everyone."

Leaving Carruthers to sit alone on his bench and stare at the falling leaves, Emily and Eugene went on with their stroll through the park.

"There must be something that we can do to cheer him up," said Emily. "If Carruthers keeps acting this way, he won't have any friends left."

"That's very true," said Eugene, "because no one likes a grouch."

So the two friends plopped down on a bench and thought long and hard.

"Well," Eugene said, "whenever I'm feeling grumpy, I listen to beautiful music."

"That gives me an idea," exclaimed Emily. "Come with me."

The two friends hurried home. In a few minutes, they were both back in the park. Emily had her tuba, and Eugene had his drum.

They found Carruthers still sitting in the same place. Ever so quietly, they tiptoed up behind him.

Emily played the tuba softly at first and then loudly, while Eugene tapped on his drum.

Carruthers put his paws to his ears and growled, "That is the worst noise I've ever heard in my life!"

Then he got up and walked away.

Emily and Eugene looked at each other. "Maybe we should have practiced more," said Eugene.

Emily sat down. "Just because we couldn't make Carruthers feel better with our music, we cannot give up. We must think of another way."

"Yes," agreed Eugene, "we must not give up."

So once again, they both thought long and hard.

"I know," said Emily, "let's ask him to have lunch with us."

"Of course! What a great idea," said Eugene. "Let's go to your house right away and send him an invitation."

Carruthers was an even bigger grouch when he came home and found the invitation to lunch. He did not feel like visiting—but what bear can stay away from food? So of course he went.

At Emily's house, Carruthers plopped down in the very best chair and watched as Eugene helped Emily serve lunch.

"It's another beautiful day, isn't it?" said Emily.

"Not really," said Carruthers.

"You must enjoy taking a stroll in the park," said Eugene.

"No, not really," said Carruthers.

"My, how lovely your fur looks today, Carruthers," said Emily.

"I've never cared for it," said Carruthers.

Emily and Eugene didn't know what else to say since Carruthers was acting so unpleasant.

When Carruthers finished eating, he said, "Thank you for the meal, but I must leave now. I need to get some fresh air."

"Then why don't we all go for a drive?" said
Eugene.

"What a good idea!" exclaimed Emily. "I'm sure
a ride out in the country will make Carruthers feel
great."

Before Carruthers could say anything at all, he
found himself sitting in the back seat of Emily's
car.

Very soon the three friends were sailing through
the open countryside.

"There's nothing like a drive in the country on a
sunny day to cheer a person up," called out
Eugene.

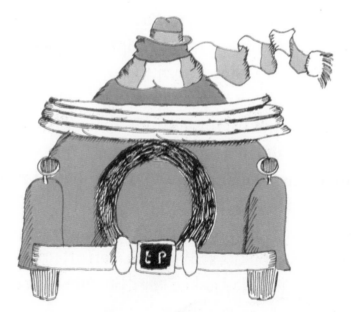

"The countryside gives me hay fever," was all Carruthers would say.

After a little while, Carruthers said, "I think it's time to go home. I'm not having a good time riding through the countryside."

Emily and Eugene were both upset. "I was hopeful that this drive would cheer him up," said Emily, "but Carruthers isn't one little bit better."

"I know," said Eugene. "I don't think there's anything else we can do but take him home."

On the way home no one spoke.

When they pulled up in front of Carruthers's house, Emily had an idea. "Carruthers," she said, "look at all those leaves in your front yard. I think we should help you rake them."

This was an idea that Carruthers did not like at all. It was not his idea of fun to rake leaves, but he went to find three rakes and a big basket.

"I don't see why we should help Carruthers rake his leaves," said Eugene.

"Sometimes keeping very busy is a good way to forget about feeling grumpy," Emily said.

When Carruthers came back, they went to work and kept very busy. Emily and Carruthers would rake leaves into the basket, and Eugene would put them into a pile. Soon the pile was very high.

19

"If we hurry," said Emily, "we will be finished in time for dinner."

But Carruthers was beginning to slow down.

He started to yawn. A small yawn at first, which
he covered with his paw. Then a much bigger yawn.
And then—a great big bear yawn.

All of a sudden, Carruthers plopped headfirst into the huge pile of leaves.

"Oh my!" cried Eugene. "What in the world has happened?"

The two friends quickly cleared away the pile of leaves and uncovered Carruthers.

"He's asleep!" they both exclaimed.

"So that is why Carruthers has been such a terrible grouch lately," said Emily. "Why didn't we think of this before? He forgot that it was time for his long winter's sleep."

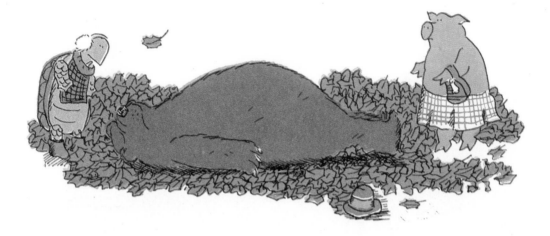

"Of course. Now I understand," said Eugene. "Carruthers should have been tucked away in bed many days ago. No wonder he has been so impossible to be around."

"There is no use waking him now," said Emily. "He'll be asleep for the rest of the winter, so it's up to us to get him into bed."

"That will be the hardest job yet," said Eugene.

After a lot of huffing and puffing, they lifted the sleeping Carruthers into a small wagon and pulled it into the house.

When they got to Carruthers's bedroom, they ever so slowly put him under the snug winter covers. Emily pulled his nightcap down around his ears. Eugene set the alarm clock for spring and pulled down the shades.

"Good night, Carruthers," whispered Emily, and she gave him a kiss on the cheek. "Sleep tight, and we'll see you in the spring when you will be your old sweet self again."

Answer these questions.

1. Why was Emily worried about Carruthers?

2. What are two of the things that Emily and Eugene did to try to cheer up Carruthers?

3. Why did Emily want to cheer up Carruthers?

4. Why had Carruthers been such a grouch?

Uncle Fonzo's Ford, Part 1

New Words

1. My uncle has a new <u>Ford</u>.
2. <u>Norma Lou</u> is my sister.
3. My name is <u>Effie</u>.
4. Class was <u>dismissed</u> at four o'clock.
5. We picked <u>dandelions</u> in the field.
6. There will be a <u>wedding</u> in the family soon.
7. He had the first <u>automobile</u> in town.
8. I have <u>already</u> been to the store.
9. The <u>entire</u> class went on a picnic.
10. The horse ate the grass in the <u>pasture</u>.

Uncle Fonzo's Ford

Miska Miles

Effie and Chester

Effie Riddle shuffled her feet under her desk.
It was almost time for school to be dismissed for
the day.

Rain was coming down very hard and
running down the windowpanes, blurring the
view of the houses beyond the school yard.

Effie's Uncle Fonzo was coming for her in his new Ford and Effie wished he wouldn't. Uncle Fonzo had a new Ford—the only automobile in town. And already, he had run out of gas three times and once he almost hit a cow in the road. Somehow, things always seemed to go wrong for Uncle Fonzo.

School was dismissed at four o'clock, when Miss Anna tapped the little bell on her desk.

"Is your uncle coming for you?" Chester asked.

"Yes he is," Effie said, "but you can't ride with him."

Chester was always ready for a ride with Uncle Fonzo. Chester liked Uncle Fonzo and Uncle Fonzo liked Chester.

Chester looked out the rain-streaked door. "I can't see him, but I hear him," he said. "He's coming up the hill. Look, he's got the top down."

Uncle Fonzo drove right up the middle of the street, cut across the school yard, and slid over to the schoolhouse steps.

"Hurry up, Effie," he said. "I don't dare stall the motor. Get in, Effie. You, too, Chester."

Effie and Chester climbed in while Uncle Fonzo explained about the top. "I was putting the side curtains up to keep out the rain, and the top fell down. I couldn't get it up again and I didn't want to keep you waiting." The rain was coming down hard.

Uncle Fonzo looked at the boys and girls who were still standing in the doorway.

"You, there," Uncle Fonzo said. "Anybody coming for you?—No?—Well, this back seat will take five with no trouble at all. Get in. Hurry up."

Uncle Fonzo pulled the lever that fed gas to his automobile, and the automobile suddenly jerked as it started to move.

Everybody in the automobile was laughing except Effie. She hunched low into her sweater. She had never been so embarrassed in her entire life.

"We'll take Effie home first," Uncle Fonzo said as they bounced along the middle of the slippery street.

He stopped the car at the Riddle house and
Effie jumped down and ran around the house.
They were still laughing in the automobile, and
Uncle Fonzo was laughing loudest of all.

Effie opened the back door and stood
dripping on the floor.

"Goodness," said Grandma. "What
happened?"

"Uncle Fonzo was trying to put on the side
curtains to keep out the rain, and the top of the
automobile fell down—"

"And Fonzo couldn't get the top back up
again!" Grandma laughed. "Wouldn't you
know it!"

"Get those wet things off," Mama said. "Right now. Get into dry clothes—"

"A little rain never hurt anybody," Grandma said.

"It's not just the rain, Grandma," Effie said. "It's what they'll say and how they'll laugh at Uncle Fonzo for coming with the top down in the rain."

And that's the way it was at school all week long. Every time there was a gray cloud in the sky, somebody said, "Do you think your Uncle Fonzo will come to get you today, Effie?" Then the entire class laughed.

When school was dismissed on Friday, Effie hurried home. Mama opened the door, and Effie asked, "Where's Grandma?"

"She wanted some exercise, so she went to the store for flour," Mama said.

Then Grandma came wheeling around the corner of the house and propped her bicycle against the porch. Effie helped Grandma with her packages.

Then Effie went outside again to look at the pink and yellow sky while she thought about the things she enjoyed here. She liked the sunset, and she liked bluebirds singing in the dogwood trees—but she didn't like Chester Burr.

She remembered the first time she saw him. The Riddles had just moved into the big white two-story house, and Uncle Fonzo had given her a big cowgirl hat.

Effie was standing by the fence, wishing that she had a horse to go with the hat, when Chester rode up on old Fanny. Effie had been ready to be friendly.

"Where's your horse?" he asked. "I'll bet you've never ridden a horse in your entire life."

At that moment Effie hated Chester.

"I could ride a horse any time I wanted to," she said. "I could ride a better horse than your ugly old horse."

Chester turned Fanny in a tight circle and Effie watched him ride away.

On Saturday morning, right after breakfast, Mama said, "There's nothing that makes better eating than the fresh, green leaves of dandelions. Effie, take a paring knife and the basket. There are plenty of good dandelions near the fence in the pasture."

"I don't like to go into Chester Burr's pasture," Effie said.

"It's not Chester's pasture," Grandma said. "It's his father's."

So Effie was picking dandelions. She didn't mind picking them, but she hoped that Chester wouldn't come riding up to find her there in his father's pasture.

Effie hurried to fill her basket. She glanced over her shoulder to be sure that Chester wasn't trotting across the pasture on old Fanny. Chester wasn't in sight.

Effie hurried to the house and slammed the door behind her. She set the basket of dandelion greens on the table.

"They look nice, Effie," Grandma said.

Effie's big sister, Norma Lou, came into the room.

"Well, Norma Lou," Grandma said, "it won't be long before we'll be having the first wedding in this family since your mother and father were married."

Effie sidled out through the back door and sat on the porch. Inside the house, they would be discussing the plans for Norma Lou's wedding. Effie knew the plans by heart because she had already heard them a million times.

Norma Lou would wear Grandma's wedding dress. Uncle Fonzo would drive over at exactly seven o'clock and he would pick up everybody but Grandma. Grandma had already told them that she would ride to church on her bicycle as she always did.

Inside, Norma Lou had raised her voice. "Grandma," she was saying, "I wish just *once* you'd go with Uncle Fonzo and the rest of us in the automobile."

"If I bother to get dressed up to go somewhere," Grandma said, "I want to be sure that I am going to get where I want to go."

"*Please,* Grandma!"

There was silence from the house. Grandma wasn't answering. Grandma didn't trust either the Ford or Uncle Fonzo's driving.

Answer these questions.

1. Why did Uncle Fonzo come to the school in the rain with the top down?
2. Why didn't Effie want to go into Chester Burr's pasture?
3. Why didn't Grandma want to go with Uncle Fonzo?

Uncle Fonzo's Ford, Part 2

New Words

1. We went <u>downstairs</u> to eat breakfast.
2. The horse <u>galloped</u> across the field.
3. I have a new <u>straw</u> hat.
4. I put a flower on the <u>brim</u> of my hat.
5. I talked with my friend on the <u>telephone</u>.
6. His voice sounds <u>familiar</u>.
7. The <u>cherry blossoms</u> on the tree are beautiful.

Uncle Fonzo's Ford

Fanny

When Effie got home from school that next Friday, Mama was talking to Grandma in a loud voice. Anyone could tell that Mama was mad. She pointed to the empty vegetable basket. "I'd just like to get my hands on that boy, Chester," she said.

Effie was interested that Chester was in trouble. "What did Chester do?" she asked.

"The fence is down and his horse trampled my lettuce into the ground," Mama said. *"Into the ground,"* she repeated. "There is not a leaf left."

Effie walked out to see the broken fence. It was really down, all the way between two posts. Effie heard a too familiar whinny. Then old Fanny galloped over the hill.

Fanny was coming by herself and she was coming fast. It looked as though she knew exactly where the break in the fence was, and planned to go straight through and finish the damage she had already done to the garden.

Effie waved her arms as Fanny headed straight for the garden. Fanny slid to a stop and reached out and nuzzled Effie's shoulder. Effie had to laugh. She had no idea that Fanny was so friendly.

She wished that there were a saddle on Fanny's back. She had never ridden a horse in her entire life—and here was a friendly horse who liked her.

She looked at the gate. Maybe she could climb up on the gate and slide over on Fanny's back from there.

Effie started for the gate and Fanny followed close behind her. When Fanny angled around a bit, Effie reached out a leg. Then she was over—

She was on a horse! It was as easy as that. Her heart beat fast. She sat there a minute and then she flapped her heels against Fanny's sides. Fanny turned and started off in a slow walk, but then she started to trot.

Then suddenly, Fanny changed her gait and galloped along slowly. Effie braced herself with her elbows, sat upright, and held fast to Fanny's mane. Then she saw that Fanny was heading straight for her own barnyard, and Chester was sitting there on the gate.

He jumped down. "I didn't think you could stick on, Effie."

Effie was too embarrassed to talk. She slid to the ground. She could only remember that she had called Fanny ugly, and she knew Chester would remember it too. She started to run, stumbling, running, stumbling again.

"Hey, wait," Chester said. "You can ride back. We can ride double—"

Effie hardly heard him as she ran home as fast as she could.

When the morning of the wedding came, Papa was painting shutters on the second story. Uncle Fonzo came by to see if he could help Papa.

Mama was putting in the hem of the dress that Effie would wear. It was white with little pink flowers all over it. The sash was pink and it hung to the hem.

Effie had a new hat. It was a plain straw with a pink band around the crown.

Effie tried on the new dress and the straw hat, then went downstairs and hurried outside to show her father. He was cleaning the paint from his brush, and Uncle Fonzo was admiring the job from the top of the ladder.

"Papa, look at me."

Just at that moment, Uncle Fonzo knocked over a can of paint and Effie's straw hat caught it on the brim.

Effie went inside, tears stinging her eyes. "Look, Mama. I can't wear my hat. It's got three green spots of paint on the brim."

"Fonzo?" Mama asked.

Effie nodded and started to cry.

Her mother looked at the dress and the hat. "I think it's only on the brim of your hat."

Uncle Fonzo came up the stairs two at a time. "I didn't know there was paint in that can," he said. "Don't cry, Effie. I'm sorry."

Effie wiped her eyes with the back of her hand.

"Couldn't you put real flowers on the brim to cover up those paint spots?" Uncle Fonzo asked. "Cherry blossoms might look real nice."

"Yes, that's it," Grandma said. "Bunches of real cherry blossoms with just a few leaves. The hat will be beautiful."

Fonzo got the cherry blossoms and Grandma got some pins. Six bunches of cherry blossoms covered the paint. Effie tried on the hat.

Mama touched her shoulder. "You look every bit as beautiful as Norma Lou," she said.

"Fine," Uncle Fonzo said.

Effie turned to Uncle Fonzo and threw her arms around his waist. "Uncle Fonzo, I could never stay mad at you. I'm sorry I was mad at all." She hugged him tightly.

Uncle Fonzo clapped her on the back. "That's all right. Let go, now. I've got to get along and do the rest of my chores. I'll see you at seven o'clock straight up. I don't want anybody to be late."

Mama and Grandma were helping Norma Lou get ready and Effie was sitting on the foot of the bed, watching. When the telephone rang, Effie ran downstairs to answer it; it was Uncle Fonzo.

"Listen, Effie, I'll be five or ten minutes late. I'm putting those new parts in the Ford, and I'm not quite finished. I'll telephone you just before I start."

"That was Uncle Fonzo," Effie said. "He's going to be five or ten minutes late."

Norma Lou looked as though she could cry any minute. "I don't want to be five or ten minutes late," she said.

They all went downstairs to wait by the telephone for Uncle Fonzo's call.

Even if he gets the parts in the car he'll never get here, Effie thought. He'll have a flat tire or something. Something always goes wrong when Uncle Fonzo is around. He can't help it.

Fifteen minutes passed and Uncle Fonzo hadn't called. Effie went outside to watch for him. There was no one in sight except Chester Burr and Fanny, who were trotting across the pasture.

"Didn't you go to the wedding?" Chester asked.

"We're going," Effie said. "But Uncle Fonzo isn't here. Maybe something happened to Uncle Fonzo's car—"

Chester rode up to the pasture gate. "I'll find out," he said. "I'll go to Uncle Fonzo's and I'll come back and tell you." He galloped off down the middle of the street.

Grandma came outside. "I thought I heard a familiar voice."

"You did," said Effie. "It was Chester. Chester's riding to Uncle Fonzo's house to see what happened. He'll be right back. What if Uncle Fonzo hasn't been able to get his car started?"

Grandma didn't answer.

They waited a long time. Suddenly, Effie heard that familiar whinny again, and Uncle Fonzo was saying, "Giddyap." There they were. The Ford was tied to old Fanny, and Uncle Fonzo and Chester were sitting in the front seat.

"Hurry," Fonzo said. "We're here and we don't want to be late for church." Fanny tossed her head and looked as though she were enjoying herself.

Everybody came running from the house. Uncle Fonzo was sitting up straight and stiff behind the wheel. Effie's heart almost burst with love for him.

"Move over here, Chester," she said. "I want to sit by my uncle."

Norma Lou, Mama, and Grandma climbed in the back seat, and Papa crowded in front. Everyone was laughing. Everyone was happy. Everyone loved everybody else. This was a wonderful night.

Effie thought about Grandma, riding in Uncle Fonzo's Ford for the first time. This was a ride that Effie would always remember.

After school on Monday, Effie would go to the pasture for dandelions. And perhaps Chester would ask her again if she wanted to ride Fanny—that would be perfect.

Answer these questions.

1. Why was Mama mad?

2. What happened to Effie's hat?

3. Why couldn't Effie stay mad at her Uncle Fonzo?

4. What did Effie hope would happen after school on Monday?

Byline: Nellie Bly

New Words

1. <u>Nellie</u> was a brave woman.
2. He was the <u>editor</u> of the newspaper.
3. She wanted to be a <u>reporter</u>.
4. Sometimes her job was <u>dangerous</u>.
5. <u>Although</u> she was tired, she kept working.
6. She lived in <u>Pittsburgh</u> for many years.
7. Her last name was <u>Cochrane</u>.
8. <u>Eighty</u> comes right after seventy-nine.
9. <u>Ocean</u> birds sometimes eat fish.
10. <u>England</u> seemed far away.

Byline: Nellie Bly

Jeanette Cook

For many years most women worked only at home. Their job was to cook food and clean house and take care of children. But in the late 1800s, a few women started looking for work outside the home. This made many people angry.

One day a Pittsburgh newspaper had a story that said that a woman should work only at home. Many people who read the story wrote letters to the editor. Most of them agreed with the story.

But one well-written letter did not agree with the story. It said that because America did not use the minds of its women, it was not as strong as it could be. The name at the end of the letter was E. Cochrane.

The editor thought the letter was very good. It had given him something to think about. In a newspaper story he asked E. Cochrane to come and talk to him about a job. To his surprise, it was not a man but a young woman who came to see him. She said that her name was E. Cochrane . . . Elizabeth Cochrane.

Elizabeth needed a job. She had to make a living for herself and her mother. Her family thought that she should be a nurse or a teacher. But Elizabeth wanted to be a reporter.

There had never been a woman reporter at that newspaper before. At first the editor tried to say no to Elizabeth. But after he heard her ideas for stories, he said that he would give her a chance.

Elizabeth began to write exciting stories. On each story she put the name Nellie Bly. This name soon became hers.

Women reporters for other newspapers wrote stories about flowers and dresses. But not Nellie. She wanted to help poor people. She sometimes went to dangerous places to get her stories.

At first many readers were upset. They thought it was not right for a young woman to go to such dangerous places. They said it was a man's job to write about a jail or about poor people who had no homes. But more and more people began to read the stories by Nellie Bly.

In the 1800s factories were not safe. When Nellie wrote that factories were dangerous places to work, the owners of the factories became angry. Nellie's editor was worried. He didn't want Nellie to get hurt, so he gave her something less dangerous to do. Nellie began writing about plays and dances.

These stories were easy to write, but Nellie could not forget the poor people who needed her help. At last she left Pittsburgh and began looking for a job as a reporter in New York City.

Many people in New York City had heard of the woman reporter from Pittsburgh, but only one person wanted to give her a job. Joseph Pulitzer was happy to put Nellie to work on his newspaper, the *World*.

Although Nellie's brave ways often upset people, Pulitzer liked her stories. Soon Nellie was again writing stories that helped poor people.

To get her stories, Nellie sometimes pretended to be someone else. She lived with poor people, worked in factories, and even had herself put in jail. This is why readers could believe the things she said in her stories.

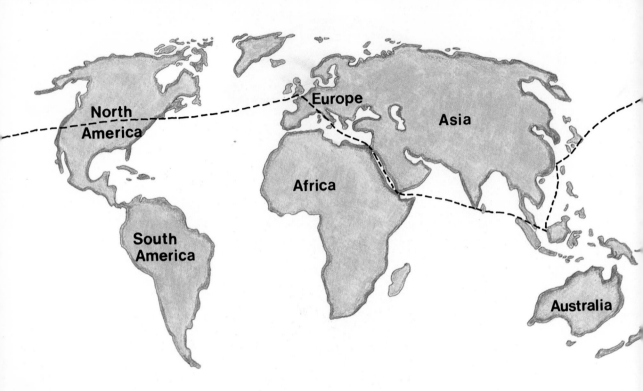

Although Nellie wrote many stories that helped people, she became best known for her trip around the world. She had read Jules Verne's *Around the World in Eighty Days,* a make-believe story about a man who went around the world in eighty days. Although going around the world in only eighty days sounded impossible, Nellie thought that it could be done. Joseph Pulitzer agreed with her. He gave her money for the trip.

On November 14, 1889, at 9:40 A.M., Nellie left New Jersey on a steamship headed for England. The steamship crossed the Atlantic Ocean and landed on a southern shore of England.

From England, Nellie sailed to France. Jules Verne came to greet her and wish her luck. Then she rode a train to Italy.

Nellie boarded another steamship to travel across the Mediterranean Sea, the Suez Canal, and the Red Sea. Then she went across the Indian Ocean and on to China and Japan.

All along the way she sent back stories about her trip. These stories were used in the *World*. Soon many people had learned of Nellie's race against time. Each day they looked in the *World* for a story by Nellie. Would Nellie make it?

In Japan, Nellie boarded a steamship to cross the Pacific Ocean. When the ship landed in San Francisco, thousands of people were there to greet Nellie. She was filled with joy.

Then Nellie crossed the United States by train. Each time the train stopped, hundreds of people were there to meet Nellie. They had to see Nellie to believe the exciting stories they had read.

On January 26, 1890, at 3:15 P.M., Nellie was back in New Jersey. She had gone around the world faster than any other person. It took her seventy-two days, six hours, and eleven minutes.

And it all started with Elizabeth Cochrane's letter to an editor.

Answer these questions.

1. Why didn't the editor of the Pittsburgh newspaper want to hire Elizabeth?

2. What name did Elizabeth Cochrane use when writing stories?

3. What did Nellie hope to do by writing stories about factories and jails?

4. Why was Nellie Bly's trip around the world so important?

Old Blue

New Words

1. The herd ran in a big circle.
2. The <u>hooves</u> of the cattle pounded in the dirt.
3. The <u>longhorn</u> cattle followed Old Blue.
4. The <u>steer</u> was like a pet to Davy.
5. <u>Texas</u> is a large state.
6. "Look out! It's a <u>stampede</u>!" he shouted.
7. I like to have eggs for <u>breakfast</u>.
8. Jeff said, "<u>Pa</u> can make chairs."
9. The woman <u>guided</u> us around the zoo.
10. Adam likes to eat <u>biscuits</u>.

Old Blue

Sibyl Hancock

"Wake up, boy!" Cookie called.

Davy opened his eyes. Cookie was standing over him. "I'll be right there," Davy said. He pushed aside his blanket and folded it to make a bedroll.

The cowboys sleeping in a circle around the campfire would soon wake up hungry for breakfast. And the cowboys riding in from watching the cattle all night would be hungry, too.

A big longhorn steer, with a hide so black it looked blue, came up to Davy.

"Old Blue," Davy said softly, "are you hungry too?" Old Blue shook his widespread horns. Davy laughed. "You think you're better than all those other longhorns. Who ever heard of a big old steer sleeping around the campfire with the cowboys!"

He rubbed Old Blue's shiny forehead. "You're a smart old steer. Not many steers can lead all the rest of the cattle on a trail drive."

Davy hurried over to the chuck wagon to help Cookie. He was frying bacon in a black skillet over the fire. "Pa said I can ride today!" Davy said.

He would be riding up front with the cowboys who guided the longhorn cattle over the trail. And if Pa said it was okay for him to ride, then it was, because Pa was the trail boss.

"You're a lucky boy," Cookie said. "But right now there's plenty to do here. Let's get to work!" He handed Davy some tin plates to set out.

"Come and get it!" Cookie yelled.

While the cowboys crowded around the chuck wagon, Davy finished his breakfast. He took some food to Old Blue. The big steer was still eating biscuits and bacon when Pa brought a horse for Davy to ride.

"Let's get moving," Pa said. "You watch what you're doing up at the front with Old Blue."

"Yes, sir," Davy said.

Davy put on his hat. He climbed onto his horse and followed Old Blue up to the head of the herd.

One of the cowboys gave the old Texas call, "Ho, cattle, ho, ho, ho, ho!" Soon all the steers were strung in a line a mile long behind Old Blue.

Davy watched Old Blue walk on to the north. No one understood how Old Blue knew which way to go.

Sometimes Old Blue walked too fast, and the lead cowboys had to slow him down.

"I don't like the looks of the sky," one of the cowboys said. "It could be a storm."

Davy looked at the sky. A storm might bring icy weather, and they had a long way to go.

They had left Texas a week ago. It would take two months to take the herd from Texas to Kansas.

Davy guided his horse along. Dirt crunched under hooves and rose in little clouds.

Davy looked at the big steer. "Old Blue, you've got your work cut out for you. Here comes the river, and we have to cross it before the wind turns."

The water was icy, but Old Blue guided the cattle right in. Cattle and cowboys followed.

The icy cold water splashed onto Davy's face. Davy held on to his horse.

"Keep going," he said. His horse began to swim. It seemed like a long time before they reached the other side of the river.

As the cattle came out of the cold water, they started running to get warm. The hooves of the longhorns pounded the rough ground.

"Let them run!" Pa shouted.

Old Blue would slow them down soon.

By late afternoon the sky grew dark. Lightning flashed, and thunder boomed. There was another sound, too. Horns rattled together, and hooves pounded the dirt.

"Stampede!" Pa cried. "Get out of the way, Davy!" he yelled.

Davy rode his horse away from the running
steers. He watched the cowboys guide Old Blue
around in a circle. The cattle followed. Soon most of
the herd were running in a big circle, which was the
only way to stop a stampede.

Davy rode back to camp.

Cookie was at the chuck wagon building a
fire.

"Get your coat on," Cookie said. "It's going to be
a bad night."

Davy put on his coat and ate some cold biscuits
and beans.

"The wind is cold," Davy said.

Pa rode up to the chuck wagon. "We'll need everyone to ride tonight," he said. "We can't let those longhorns stampede again."

"Do you want me to ride?" Davy asked.

Pa nodded. "I can use your help."

Davy pulled his hat lower over his eyes and rode out with the other cowboys.

Late that night, the rain turned to sleet.

If the longhorns stampeded in this storm, some could get lost and freeze before they were found.

It was the longest night Davy could ever remember. The sleet turned to snow, and Davy couldn't even see Old Blue.

By daylight, the worst of the storm was over. The cowboys took turns eating breakfast. Davy stood by the fire trying to get warm.

"You okay, Davy?" Pa asked.

"Just cold," Davy said. "Look who's here."

Old Blue came close for some biscuits. "Old Blue, I almost lost you last night," Davy said, rubbing the steer's forehead.

"When we get to Kansas City, I'm going to buy you a big bell to wear around your neck. Then I'll always know where you are," Davy said. "And so will the cattle."

"No one has ever put a bell on a lead steer," Pa said, "but no steer was ever as tame as Old Blue. It's a good idea if it works."

"Davy, you don't have to wait until Kansas City. I've got a bell you can use," Cookie said. "I'll get it." He came back with a bell and a piece of rope.

Davy tied the bell around Old Blue's neck. "There you go, Old Blue. How do you like that?"

Old Blue shook his horns and listened to the bell clang.

"Just look how proud that old steer is," said Pa, laughing.

Davy gave Old Blue a hug. Old Blue shook his horns again and rang the bell louder than before.

If a longhorn could smile, Old Blue would have.

Answer these questions.

1. What was Old Blue?
2. What did the cattle do after they crossed the river?
3. What did Davy put around Old Blue's neck?
4. What was so unusual about Old Blue?

Write on your own.

Pretend that you are Davy. You are writing what happens every day on the cattle drive. It is the day after Old Blue gets his bell. Write what happens that day.

Speaking of Cows

Speaking of cows
(Which no one was doing)
Why are they always
Staring and chewing?
Staring at people,
Chewing at clover,
Doing the same things
Over and over?

Once in a while,
You see a cow mooing,
Swishing her tail
At a fly that needs shooing.
Most of the time, though,
What's a cow doing?
Munching and looking,
Staring and chewing.

Eyes never blinking,
Jaws always moving,
What are cows thinking?
What are they *proving?*

Cows mustn't care for
New ways of doing.
That's what they stare for;
That's why they're chewing.

Kaye Starbird

Words to Know for First Aid

If someone is hurt, you might need to read these words. These words will help you know more about first aid.

bandage   fracture
compresses   ointment
antiseptic soap   wound
external use only   splint

Which "First Aid" words make sense in these sentences? Write the sentences on your paper.

1. If the skin is cut or torn, it is called a _____.

2. _____ is used to clean a wound.

3. An antiseptic _____ is put on a wound to help it heal.

4. A _____ is used to cover a wound.

5. A _____ is a break in a bone.

6. If a person has a fracture, a _____ may be used to keep the broken ends from moving.

7. _____ means you must not put it in your mouth.

8. Cold, wet pads of cloth called _____ may be placed on sunburns or other slight burns.

EXPERIENCES

Through Grandpa's Eyes

New Words

1. The music was written using all <u>sharps</u>.
2. The water is <u>gurgling</u> over the rocks in the stream.
3. He cannot see the picture because he is <u>blind</u>.
4. There were six <u>flats</u> in the tune she played.
5. She played a large instrument called a <u>cello</u>.

Through Grandpa's Eyes

Patricia MacLachlan

Of all the houses that I know, I like my grandpa's best. Grandpa's house is my favorite because I see it through Grandpa's eyes.

Grandpa is blind. He doesn't see the house the way I do, but he has his own way of seeing.

In the morning, the sun pushes through the curtains into my eyes. I burrow down into the covers to get away, but the light follows me. I give up, throw back the covers, and run to Grandpa's room.

The sun wakes Grandpa differently from the way it wakes me. He says it touches him, *warming* him awake. When I peek around the door, Grandpa is already up and doing his morning exercises by the bed. He stops and smiles because he hears me.

"Good morning, John."

"Where's Nana?" I ask him.

"Don't you know?" he says. "Close your eyes, John, and look through my eyes."

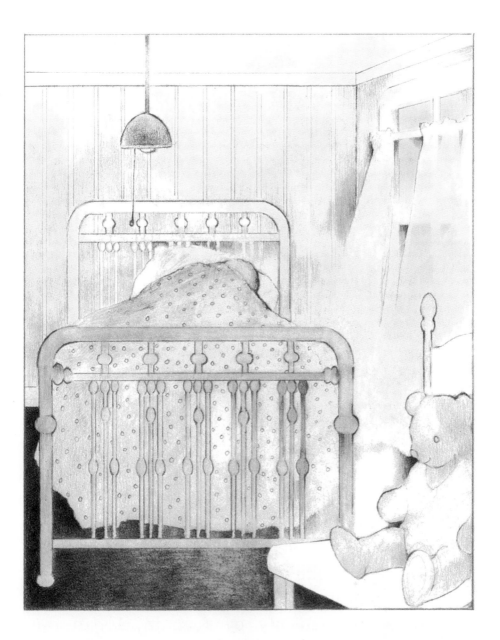

I close my eyes. Down below, I hear the
banging of pots and the gurgling sound of water
running that I didn't hear before.

"Nana is in the kitchen, fixing breakfast,"
I say.

When I open my eyes again, I can see Grandpa nodding at me. He is tall with dark gray hair, and his eyes are sharp blue even though they are not sharp seeing.

"I smell eggs frying," says Grandpa, "and toast."

We follow the stairway with its worn wooden banister and go down into the kitchen.

When he eats, Grandpa's plate of food is a clock.

"Two eggs at nine o'clock and toast at two o'clock," says Nana to Grandpa.

I make my plate of food a clock, too, and eat through Grandpa's eyes.

After breakfast, I follow Grandpa's path to the living room, to the window that he opens to feel the weather outside, and to his cello in the corner.

"Will you play your cello with me, John?" he asks.

He tunes our cellos without looking. I play with a music stand and music before me. I know all about sharps and flats because I see them on the music. But Grandpa plays the sharps and flats. They are in his fingers. For a moment I close my eyes and play through Grandpa's eyes. My fingering hand slides up and down the cello neck—toward the pegs for flats, toward the bridge for sharps. But with my eyes closed my bow falls from the strings.

"Listen," says Grandpa, "and I'll play a piece I learned when I was your age. It was my favorite."

He plays the tune while I listen. That is the way Grandpa learns new pieces—by listening.

Later, Nana joins us.

"The river is up," says Nana.

Grandpa nods a short nod. "It rained again last night. Did you hear the gurgling in the rain gutter?"

Grandpa and I walk outside, through the front yard and across the field to the river. Grandpa has not been blind forever. He remembers in his mind the gleam of the sun on the river and the Queen Anne's lace in the meadow, but he gently takes my elbow as we walk so that I can help show him the path.

"I feel a south wind," says Grandpa.

I can tell which way the wind is blowing because I see the way the tops of the trees lean. Grandpa tells by the feel of the meadow grasses and by the way his hair blows against his face.

When we come to the riverbank, I see that Nana was right. The water is high and has cut in by the willow tree. It is flowing around and gurgling over the roots of the tree. I see a blackbird with a red patch on its wing sitting on a cattail. Without thinking about Grandpa being blind, I point my finger.

"What is that bird, Grandpa?" I ask excitedly.

"Conk-a-ree," the bird calls to us.

"A red-winged blackbird," says Grandpa.

He can't see my finger pointing, but he hears the song of the bird.

Nana calls from the front porch of the house.

"Nana's made hot bread for lunch," he tells me happily.

I close my eyes, but all I can smell is the wet earth by the river.

As we walk back to the house, Grandpa stops suddenly. He bends his head to one side, listening, and points his finger upward.

"Honkers," he whispers.

I look up and see a flock of geese, high in the clouds, flying in a V.

"Canada geese," I tell him.

"Honkers," he insists and we both laugh.

In the afternoon, Grandpa, Nana, and I take our books outside to read under the apple tree. Grandpa reads his book with his fingers, feeling the raised Braille dots that tell him the words.

After supper, Grandpa turns on the television. I watch, but Grandpa listens, and the music and the words tell him when something is dangerous or funny, happy or sad.

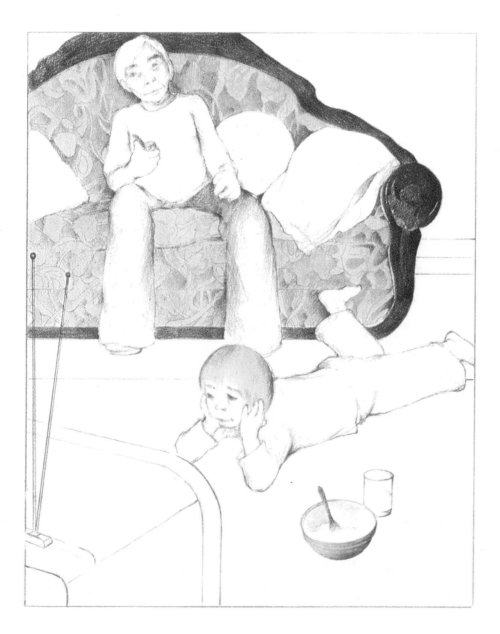

Somehow, Grandpa knows when it is dark,
and he takes me upstairs and tucks me into bed.
He bends down to kiss me, his hands feeling my
head.

"You need a haircut, John," he says.

Before Grandpa leaves, he pulls the light chain above my bed to turn out the light. But, by mistake, he's turned it on instead. I lie for a moment after he's gone, smiling, before I get up to turn off the light.

Then, when it is dark for me the way it is dark for Grandpa, I hear the night noises that Grandpa hears. The house creaking, the birds singing their last songs of the day, the wind rustling the tree outside my window.

Then, all of a sudden, I hear the sounds of geese overhead. They fly low over the house.

"Grandpa," I call softly, hoping he's heard them too.

"Honkers," he calls back.

"Go to sleep, John," says Nana.

Grandpa says her voice smiles to him. I test it.

"What?" I call to her.

"I said go to sleep," she answers.

She says it sternly, but Grandpa is right. Her voice smiles to me. I know. Because I'm looking through Grandpa's eyes.

Answer these questions.

1. How does Grandpa say the sun wakes him up?

2. When he eats, how is Grandpa's plate of food arranged?

3. How can John tell which way the wind is blowing?

4. How does Grandpa tell which way the wind is blowing?

5. How did Grandpa know that the bird was a red-winged blackbird if he couldn't see it?

Write on your own.

One day, Grandpa and John go to the grocery store. Write three sentences that describe what John sees. Then write three sentences that describe the same thing as John would see it through Grandpa's eyes.

Eye Sights

Green eyes are like emerald jewels,
Blue eyes look like liquid pools,
Brown eyes big as mother earth,
Bright eyes shine for all they're worth.
Eyes like sponges soak life up
They give things shape that you can't touch
And if you want to squeeze them dry
Eyes will even let you cry.
Eyes tell people when you're sad,
When you're mad, and when you're glad,
Eyes like windows let in light,
But eyes can give you more than sight.

Mark F. Evans

Katy Did It, Part 1

New Words

1. <u>She'd</u> be home by six o'clock.
2. The flower was tiny and <u>delicate</u>.
3. A <u>boulder</u> is a huge rock.
4. <u>Katy</u> lives next door.
5. <u>Toby</u> is a friendly dog.
6. I sat <u>beside</u> my best friend.
7. <u>Milonas</u> is her last name.
8. I <u>embroidered</u> a flower on my dress.
9. I have a new <u>suede</u> coat.
10. We cut the apple in <u>half</u>.

Katy Did It

Victoria Boutis

Katy's Package

The family had finished their supper. Mr. Milonas was sitting on the living room couch leafing through one of his favorite books, *The Adirondack High Peaks*. He patted the spot next to him and Katy plopped down beside him.

"There's a three-day weekend coming up," Mr. Milonas said. "Is anyone interested in going on a hike with me?"

Mrs. Milonas looked up from her crossword puzzle. "I'd love to," she began, "but I'd better stay home and study for my history final that's coming up."

Katy's brother Josh had wandered in from the kitchen. "I'd like to do some climbing, but that's the weekend of the soccer play-offs. I won't be able to go either."

Mr. Milonas looked at Katy and said, "How about you, Katy-did? Do you have something else planned, too?"

Katy laughed and shook her head.

Mr. Milonas opened the book and asked, "How about Big Dix?"

Katy leaned over her father's arm to read about Big Dix. "4,857 feet," she murmured. "That's a lot of feet for one mountain."

"Yes," Mr. Milonas said. "It *is* one of the highest, but the trail is not too difficult. There is a steep section near the summit, but by that time you'll be in such good shape you'll skip to the top. What do you say? Shall we hike it together?—you, me, and Toby, of course."

The thought of climbing a mountain with just her father and her dog made Katy tingly with excitement. She'd be a real hiker then. "Yes, I'll go with you," she said.

Katy grinned because her father wanted her for his hiking partner. That was great, and she'd skip up Big Dix, just like he said.

———

When Katy returned from school a few days later, there was a package on the front step with a label that said: Miss Katy Milonas. "It's for me!" she shouted.

Toby jumped up, put his paws on Katy's shoulders, and lapped at her face. "Hi, Toby," Katy said. "Look what I got—a package!"

Katy tore off all the tape and brown paper that was wrapped around the package. When the box was open, Katy looked inside and breathed out a long "Ooooooh." In the box was a pair of hiking boots. They were soft gray suede, and embroidered at each ankle was a delicate yellow and white flower.

"Look, Toby. Aren't they beautiful!" Katy traced her finger over the smooth threads of the delicate embroidered flowers. "They're for our hike." A hike—Toby knew about that, and he leaped around her, yipping happily.

On the evening before the hike, Katy helped her father pack all the equipment they would need.

"I think we're all set," he said. "Up to bed now. Tomorrow will be a big day."

They left early the next morning. Katy fell asleep during the drive, and the next thing she heard was the voice of her father.

"Last stop—everybody out."

At the trail's entrance there was a place to sign their names. "We have to sign in here," Mr. Milonas said. "That way the rangers can keep track of all of us hikers."

Before they started walking, Mr. Milonas snapped a picture of Katy standing beside a huge boulder.

"We're going to follow the red trail," Mr. Milonas said. "We can tell we're on the right path because, every so often, there will be a red disk tacked to a tree."

At first the trail meandered near a small stream, and sometimes it went right through the water. Katy liked hopping from one rock to another, taking pride in keeping her suede boots with the delicate embroidered flowers dry. Soon they reached some huge rocks and found a boulder that was flat on top. The boulder made a perfect picnic table, so they stopped for lunch.

When they began walking again, Toby took the lead. The trail became steeper and more rocky. Katy had to keep her eyes on her boots so she wouldn't trip. For the first time, she was aware that she was climbing. Her breath came in short, loud pants. Her heart pounded, her legs hurt, and her backpack felt heavy on her back.

"Oh," Katy groaned, "how much farther?"

"Just another half mile," her father said.

"Another half mile," Katy said to herself as she lifted one heavy foot and then the other. "Just another half mile."

Katy saw a drop splat on the tip of her boot. It spread into a nickel-sized dark spot on the gray suede.

"Let's hurry," Mr. Milonas said. "I think it's starting to rain."

Mr. Milonas helped her get out the red poncho he had told her to pack "just in case."

With the rain coming down, Katy couldn't hike as fast as her father and she had trouble keeping up with him. "This isn't any fun," Katy said to herself.

The rain made Toby slow down, too. He walked beside Katy now, and stopped every few minutes to shake the water from his coat.

"That wasn't so bad, was it?" Mr. Milonas said as Katy dragged herself up to the place where they would set up their camp.

Katy's feet hurt, her shoulders were sore, and she was hungry.

After supper, when it became dark, Mr. Milonas lit the candle lantern. Katy stared into its circle of light as she tried to cover a yawn with her hand.

"I'll bet you're tired," Mr. Milonas said. "Tomorrow will be better. You just need a good night's sleep."

Katy went into the tent and slipped quickly into her sleeping bag because of the cold.

"Good night," her father said. "I'll be right here if you need me."

Toby came in through the tent flap, turned around twice, and flopped down beside her. Katy curled up inside the bag and squeezed her eyes shut, but she couldn't sleep. A bothersome thought began to take form in her mind—maybe she'd never be a real hiker. A lonely tear rolled down her cheek and into her hair.

Answer these questions.

1. What kind of equipment do you think Katy and her father packed for their hike in the mountains?

2. What was in the package labeled "Miss Katy Milonas"?

3. Where were Katy and Toby going?

4. How did Katy feel when she got to the place where they would set up camp?

5. What bothersome thought kept Katy from falling asleep?

Katy Did It, Part 2

New Words

1. "Good morning," he said <u>cheerfully</u>.
2. I was glad when we <u>finally</u> got home.
3. John quickly <u>replied</u> to the teacher's question.
4. She felt as <u>though</u> she could win the race this time.
5. <u>Brisk</u> and cool was how Jeff said the air felt.
6. I like <u>oatmeal</u> for breakfast.
7. We set up our tents at the <u>campsite</u>.
8. I took his picture with my <u>camera</u>.

Katy Did It

The Mountaintop Surprise

Katy woke to the sounds of breakfast pots clanging. Then she remembered that she had slept out all night. She smiled at the thought.

"Well, good morning," Mr. Milonas said cheerfully. Katy's father was always cheerful in the morning.

Katy hopped from one foot to another. "It's freezing," she said.

"Brisk," her father replied cheerfully. "A marvelous, brisk morning." He handed Katy her cup. It was heaped with oatmeal and smelled delicious.

Katy ate quickly. "That was good," Katy said. Then, as though she had made an important discovery, she said, "Oatmeal is delicious."

She ate a second helping more slowly. With the oatmeal warming her insides, she had to admit that it wasn't freezing after all. Just brisk.

The air was still cool when Mr. Milonas helped Katy put on her backpack. "Ready to go?" he asked.

"Yes," Katy replied, but somehow it was hard to leave the campsite. Katy waved a silent good-bye to the campsite, then she fixed her eyes on her feet again. She had to watch carefully where she put each foot. The trail was narrow here, and there were sharp rocks that could trip her.

At the end of the day, when they finally stopped, Katy flopped down on the ground. Toby plopped down beside her and put his head on one of her arms.

"You're not tired, are you?" her father said. "We only hiked four miles today."

"Uphill," Katy noted, just before her eyelids drooped shut.

Katy ate dinner and then crawled into her tent. She slid into her sleeping bag, ducked her head under the cover, and closed her eyes.

All too soon, morning came. As they left the campsite, Katy moved slowly. The trail was gentle, but her feet felt heavy.

The trail dipped and turned. Now they were walking downhill, and the trail was so steep that Katy's legs shook as she tried to keep her feet from sliding out from under her.

Then they came to a new trail, and there was a blue disk tacked to a tree. "This way to the top," Mr. Milonas said.

The trail wasn't gentle anymore. Katy ducked under trees, slipped through mud, and climbed over rocks.

Her father and Toby had stopped up ahead to wait for her. She finally panted up to them and leaned against a boulder. Her heart pounded, so she leaned her head back and closed her eyes until the pounding stopped. "It's too hard," Katy breathed out. "I can't do it." There—she'd said it.

But her father replied cheerfully, "Sure you can, and Toby will help you." Mr. Milonas handed Katy the end of Toby's leash and Katy found that it was really true. With Toby pulling, it was easy to walk uphill. She held onto the leash and zipped past bushes and over rocks.

Soon Katy was breathless as she tried to keep pace with Toby. "Slow down, Toby," Katy said as she pulled back on his leash. She ducked quickly to avoid a branch that jutted out at eye level.

Katy was glad to hand Toby's leash back to her father. Then she kept climbing. She passed her father at a lookout point while he was taking pictures with his camera. Katy did not want to stop now. She felt an urge to reach the top.

The trail had gotten steep again and Katy was breathing hard. She didn't have Toby to help her now—each step was her own effort. She felt as though her pack were pulling her backward, but she forced herself up.

Katy climbed—right foot, breathe in, left foot, breathe out. Right foot, breathe in, left foot, breathe out. She wasn't skipping up Big Dix, but she had found a natural pace that carried her up and up until she was finally there—the top of the mountain.

The valley below was dark green and dotted with specks of red and orange. One river looked like a crooked snake coiling around a cluster of toy houses. And mountain after mountain formed waves of gray and green.

Katy had never seen anything so beautiful. Even the air was different. It was lighter somehow, and it made her feel giddy. She could see the whole circle of the earth, and felt as though she had made a great discovery: the world is round.

"You did it!" shouted Katy's father. "What a hiker!" He stood beside her and pointed out the peaks around them, telling her the name of each one. Now that Katy knew their names, it was like meeting a group of friends.

Then Mr. Milonas pointed his camera at Katy and Toby and said, "We must have a picture of this important moment." Katy smiled at the camera as she and Toby sat still for the shot. Then they ran off to explore the mountaintop.

Most of the mountaintop was smooth, rounded rock. Scattered here and there were bent, scrubby trees clinging to the mountain.

A dot of color among the gray rocks and dull green bushes caught Katy's eye. There was a patch of sandy soil between two boulders. Growing in the soil was a tiny yellow and white flower—the same flower that was embroidered on her hiking boots. "It's my flower," Katy said. She had to have it.

The flower was so small, and it was almost hidden between the rocks. No one would know. She reached out to pick the flower. But just before her fingers tugged the thin roots from the sand, something made her stop.

Katy thought of the hikers' motto that she had seen posted at the entrance of many trails: "Take nothing but pictures—leave nothing but footprints." That was the way it should be, she knew.

Katy looked at her scratched, dirty boots. They weren't beautiful anymore, but she loved them even more the way they looked now. Because now they were hiked-in hiking boots. And she was the one who had made them that way. "I did it!" Katy said. She let go of the flower.

She didn't need some dry petals pressed inside a book. She knew that, somewhere inside her, the flower would always be hers.

"I did it," she said again. With a broken twig she scratched K—A—T—Y into the sandy soil beside the flower.

Answer these questions.

1. Why did Katy smile at the thought that she had slept out all night?

2. What did the blue disk along the trail mean?

3. What was Katy surprised to find on the top of the mountain?

4. What did Katy write in the sandy soil beside the flower?

On the Trail

New Words

1. Our pizza had a <u>combination</u> of different cheeses on it.
2. Eating a good breakfast will give you lots of <u>energy</u>.
3. I like to eat <u>granola</u> after school.
4. I will give you a large <u>amount</u> of nuts to eat.
5. A <u>recipe</u> tells how to make something.
6. I listed the <u>ingredients</u> needed to make wheat bread.
7. The color green is made from a <u>mixture</u> of blue and yellow.

On the Trail

Shirley Petersen

Do you like to hike? If you do, you need some energy that will last during the long trip on the trail. This kind of energy comes from a combination of foods. Scientists have found that different kinds of food, when eaten together, give you all the energy your body needs. This combination of different foods is the idea behind the trail mix recipe. This recipe is a combination of granola or other whole grains, seeds, nuts, and fruits. When eaten together, these foods will give your body the right amount of energy needed for a long hike.

Besides being healthful, trail mix is easy to make and easy to carry. And you don't have to be on a hike to eat it. It makes a great after-school snack! Try this trail mix recipe soon—you'll like it!

TRAIL MIX

You will need:
Large bowl
Measuring cup
Wooden spoon
Plastic bags

Ingredients:

Granola (or other
    whole-grain flakes)
Sunflower seeds
Almonds
Peanuts

Walnuts or pecans
Raisins
Dried apples, peaches,
    and apricots

Directions:

1. Measure 4 cups of granola (or whole-grain flakes)
   and put this amount into the large bowl.
2. Add a large amount, about 2 cups, of sunflower
   seeds.
3. Add 1/2 cup each of shelled almonds, peanuts, and
   walnuts or pecans to the other ingredients already
   in the bowl.
4. Add 1 cup of raisins to the mixture.

5. Tear 1 small package each of dried apples, peaches, and apricots into bite-size pieces. Add to mixture in the bowl.

6. Mix all ingredients together well.

7. Scoop mixture into plastic bags and close tightly.

Answer these questions.

1. What do you need when you go on a long hike?

2. What does a combination of granola, seeds, nuts, and fruits do for your body?

3. Why can you eat trail mix even if you're not on a hike?

Muscles at Work

New Words

1. <u>Stretch</u> your arms above your head.
2. The word <u>skeletal</u> refers to your skeleton, or bones.
3. I <u>fastened</u> the papers together with tape.
4. Your <u>biceps</u> is on the front side of your upper arm.
5. Your arm bends at the <u>elbow</u>.
6. Your <u>triceps</u> is on the back side of your upper arm.
7. The cloth was as <u>smooth</u> as velvet.
8. He had sore <u>muscles</u> from playing football.
9. We have <u>blood</u> in our body.

Muscles at Work

Lee Hoyt

Don't move a muscle!

That is one order no one can follow. No matter how quiet and still you try to be, muscles are always moving in your body. Muscles are always moving your rib cage up and down so you can breathe. If you are standing still, the muscles that pull on your bones are moving so you can keep your balance. Even when you're asleep, your heart muscle is working to pump blood and the muscles that let your blood move through your body are at work.

Each person has more than six hundred muscles. A new baby has as many as a baseball player. One hundred of the muscles are in your face and neck alone, letting you laugh, close your eyes, read, and eat food.

Some of your muscles are called skeletal muscles. They are fastened to bones. The biceps muscle is fastened to your lower arm bone, below your elbow. It runs along your upper arm and is fastened at the top to a bone in your shoulder. When you bend your elbow, the biceps contracts, or gets shorter and firmer. If you press your upper arm while you are bending your elbow, you can feel the biceps as it pulls up your lower arm.

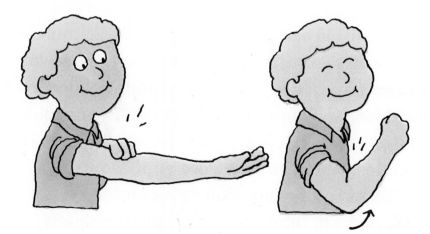

When you stretch your arm out again, you use a different muscle, the triceps. It contracts and pulls your arm back down.

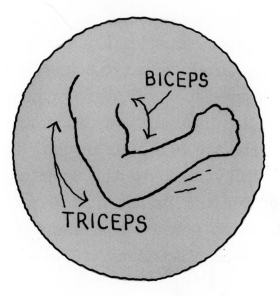

A muscle can pull, but not push. So muscles often work in pairs. The biceps and triceps work as partners. They take turns pulling when you bend and straighten your elbow. Many other muscles work together in pairs, such as the muscles that open and close your mouth.

Because of your skeletal muscles, you can walk, jump, stretch, draw pictures, and do hundreds of other things every day.

You have other muscles called smooth muscles. They work without your thinking about them.

There are smooth muscles in your eyes that change the size of your pupils. When you first go outside on a bright day, the pupil, or black opening in your eye, gets smaller because the eye doesn't need so much light. When you go into a dark room, your eye needs more light, and the pupil gets larger. Two sets of smooth muscles work in each eye to make the pupil larger or smaller. Like the biceps and triceps, these two sets of eye muscles work together.

Other smooth muscles help your body make use of the food you eat, and help the blood move through your body. The smooth muscles keep your body running well, even though you may not think about them, or even know that they are at work.

The heart is a special smooth muscle. No other muscle is exactly like it. It never stops working. Day and night it is busy pumping blood. Your heart never gets tired because it takes a quick rest after each heartbeat.

Skeletal muscles need a longer rest after they've been working hard. If they get too tired, they will stop working for a short time. If you hold something heavy for a long time, sooner or later you may have to let go of it because the skeletal muscles in your arm and hand will need to rest.

When muscles are not used enough, they get small and weak. After a broken arm or leg has been in a cast for a few weeks, it will feel very weak because its muscles have not been used. The arm or leg will need to stretch and exercise for a few days before it can be strong again.

Muscles become strong through exercise. Without exercise, a tiny baby could never grow up to be a strong baseball player. First the baby exercises by kicking and wiggling for many months. When it grows strong enough to crawl, it exercises even more. Finally it is able to pull itself up, stand alone, and take a step or two. Three hundred of its muscles must work together for the baby to take just one step. No wonder a baby falls down many times as it is learning to walk. But each time the baby pulls itself up again, it is using its muscles to grow stronger.

Muscles that are used a lot become big and strong. Someone who lifts heavy things all day will have big biceps. A bike rider will get strong leg muscles. The muscles that you use most will become the strongest.

Each of your muscles works for you in its special way, even though you may not notice it or think about it. Your muscles are always moving.

Answer these questions.

1. How many muscles does each person have?

2. Where are skeletal muscles found?

3. What are the names of the two muscles in the arm?

4. Which muscle works all the time?

5. Why is it important to exercise to keep muscles strong?

When I Read

I'm a runner, a racer,
I've got a lot of speed.
I can sprint
from here to   there
with time to spare.
But when I *read*
then I'm a diver!
I plunge
     right
          in
and until the story's over
I don't come up for air.
Then too I'm an explorer,
a tracker and a rover
and I always
find something
I didn't know was there.

Lillian Morrison

119

Words to Know for Computers

Most of us are learning about computers. If we know these words and what they mean, it will help us understand computers.

keyboard   memory
input/output   terminal
hardware   software
program   printer

Match the computer words with a set of words below. Number your paper from 1 to 6. Write the computer word beside the right number.

1. the machine that prints out information

2. the part of a terminal used to type in information or programs

3. an output machine that looks like a TV screen

4. the machinery for computing

5. another name for programs

6. a set of instructions telling a computer what to do

WISHES

Flat Stanley, Part 1

New Words

1. My brother <u>Arthur</u> is six years old.
2. I ate a peanut butter <u>sandwich</u> for lunch.
3. We saw the <u>enormous</u> elephant at the zoo.
4. I put the letter in an <u>envelope</u>.
5. I read a book by Mr. <u>Lambchop</u>.
6. I put the note on the <u>bulletin board</u>.
7. "<u>Hey</u>, come here!" he shouted.

Flat Stanley

Jeff Brown

Stanley Lambchop

Breakfast was ready. "I will go wake up the boys," Mrs. Lambchop said to her husband, George Lambchop. Just then their younger son, Arthur, shouted from the bedroom he shared with his brother Stanley.

"Hey! Come and look! Hey!"

"Hay is for horses, Arthur, not people," Mr. Lambchop said as they entered the bedroom.

Arthur pointed to Stanley's bed. Across it lay an enormous bulletin board. It had fallen, during the night, on top of Stanley.

But Stanley was not hurt. "What's going on here?" he called out cheerfully from beneath the enormous bulletin board.

Mr. and Mrs. Lambchop hurried to lift the bulletin board from the bed.

"Hey!" said Arthur. "Stanley's flat!"

"As a pancake," said Mr. Lambchop.

"Let's all have breakfast," Mrs. Lambchop said, "and then Stanley and I will go see Doctor Dan."

Soon they were in Doctor Dan's office. "How do you feel, Stanley?" Doctor Dan asked.

"I felt sort of tickly for a while after I got up," Stanley Lambchop said, "but I feel fine now."

"We'll just have to keep an eye on this young fellow," Doctor Dan said. He took Stanley's measurements.

Stanley was four feet tall, about a foot wide, and half an inch thick.

When Stanley got used to being flat, he enjoyed it.

He could go in and out of rooms, even when the door was closed, just by lying down and sliding through the crack at the bottom.

Arthur tried to slide under a door, but he just banged his head.

One day Stanley got a letter from a friend whose family had moved to California. School was out for the summer and Stanley was invited to spend a few days with his friend.

Mr. Lambchop sighed and said, "A round-trip airplane ticket to California will cost too much. I will have to think of some other way."

When Mr. Lambchop came home from the office that evening, he brought with him an enormous brown-paper envelope.

"Now then, Stanley, try this for size," he said.

The envelope fit Stanley very well. There was even room left over, Mrs. Lambchop discovered, for a sandwich made with thin bread, and a flat carton filled with milk.

The next day Mr. and Mrs. Lambchop slid Stanley into his envelope, along with the sandwich and the carton of milk, and mailed him from the box on the corner. The envelope had to be folded to fit through the slot, but Stanley was a limber boy and inside the box he straightened right up again.

Mrs. Lambchop tapped on the box and shouted, "Can you hear me, dear? Are you all right?"

Stanley's voice came quite clearly. "I'm fine. Can I eat my sandwich now?"

"Wait an hour. And try not to get too hot, dear," Mrs. Lambchop said. Then she and Mr. Lambchop cried out "Good-bye, good-bye!" and went home.

Stanley had a fine time in California, and returned home in a beautiful white air-mail envelope.

Mr. Lambchop liked to take the boys to the zoo or roller-skating in the park, but it was difficult when they were crossing streets or moving about in crowds. Stanley and Arthur would often be pushed away from his side and Mr. Lambchop worried that hurrying people might knock them down.

It was easier after Stanley got flat.

Mr. Lambchop discovered that he could roll Stanley up without hurting him at all. He would tie a piece of string around Stanley to keep him from unrolling and make a little loop in the string for himself. It was as simple as carrying a package, and he could hold Arthur with the other hand.

Stanley did not mind being carried because he had never much liked to walk. Arthur didn't like to walk either, but he had to.

One Sunday afternoon they met an old friend of Mr. Lambchop's.

"Well, George, I see you have bought some wallpaper," the man said.

"Wallpaper?" said Mr. Lambchop. "Oh, no. This is my son Stanley."

He undid the string and Stanley unrolled.

"How do you do?" Stanley said.

Mr. Lambchop rolled Stanley up again and they set out for home. It rained quite hard while they were on the way. Stanley, of course, hardly got wet at all, just around the edges, but Arthur got soaked.

Late that night Mr. and Mrs. Lambchop heard a noise out in the living room. They found Arthur lying on the floor near the bookcase. He had piled many heavy books on top of himself.

Mr. and Mrs. Lambchop sent him back to bed, but the next morning they spoke to Stanley. "Arthur can't help feeling the way he does," they said. "Be nice to him. You're his big brother, after all."

One day Stanley and Arthur were in the park. The day was sunny, but windy too, and many children were flying beautiful, enormous kites with long tails.

Arthur sighed and said, "Someday I will have a big kite and I will win a kite-flying contest and be famous like everyone else. *Nobody* knows who I am these days."

Stanley remembered what his parents had said, so he went to a boy whose kite was broken and asked to use his large spool of string.

"You can fly me, Arthur," he said.

He attached the string to himself and gave Arthur the spool to hold. He ran across the grass, sideways to get up speed, and then he turned to meet the breeze.

Up, up, up . . . UP! went Stanley, being a kite.

Arthur let out all the string and Stanley soared high above the trees.

After a while Arthur got tired of running about with the empty spool.

Some boys came up to Arthur and invited him to join them in a quick game of football. Arthur left the spool wedged in the fork of a tree. He did not notice, while he was playing football, that the wind was blowing the string and tangling it about the tree.

The string got shorter and shorter, but Stanley did not realize how low he was until leaves brushed his feet, and then it was too late. He got stuck in the branches. Many minutes passed before Arthur and the other boys heard Stanley's cries and set him free.

Answer these questions.

1. What did Stanley look like after the bulletin board was lifted off him?

2. How did Stanley get to California to visit his friend?

3. Why did Arthur pile books on top of himself?

4. What happened to Stanley while Arthur was playing football?

Flat Stanley, Part 2

New Words

1. I moved my fingers to make them <u>wiggle</u>.
2. The <u>thieves</u> broke into the bank.
3. The car was too <u>expensive</u> for me to buy.
4. We saw many famous paintings at the <u>museum</u>.
5. The <u>guards</u> watched over the paintings.
6. Nobody knew who she was in that <u>disguise</u>.
7. The <u>shepherdess</u> watched over the sheep.

Flat Stanley

Stanley's Plan

Mr. and Mrs. O. Jay Dart lived in the apartment above the Lambchops. Mr. Dart was the director of the Famous Museum of Art.

"I see," said Mr. Lambchop one morning while reading the paper, "that another painting has been stolen from the Famous Museum. Mr. Dart thinks that it was stolen by sneak thieves."

The next morning Stanley Lambchop heard Mr. Dart talking to his wife in the elevator.

"These sneak thieves work at night," Mr. Dart said. "The museum is so big that it's very difficult for our guards to guard every picture, and I fear it is hopeless."

Stanley had an idea, and he told it to Mr. Dart.

"Stanley," Mr. Dart said, "if your mother will give her permission, I will put you and your plan to work tonight!"

Mrs. Lambchop gave her permission and that evening Stanley went with Mr. Dart to the Famous Museum. Mr. Dart took him into the main hall, where the biggest and most expensive paintings were hung, and he pointed to a huge painting of a bearded man playing a violin. That, Mr. Dart explained, was the most expensive painting in the world!

Then Mr. Dart took Stanley into his office and said, "It's time for you to put on a disguise."

From a closet he took out a shepherdess disguise.

"In this shepherdess disguise," Mr. Dart said, "you'll look like a painting that belongs in the main hall."

"I'll look like a girl, that's what I will look like," Stanley said.

But he was a good sport, so he put on the disguise.

Back in the main hall, Mr. Dart helped Stanley up into an empty picture frame on the wall across from the world's most expensive painting.

The frame was a perfect fit, and against the wall Stanley looked just like a picture.

"Except for one thing," Mr. Dart said. "A shepherdess is supposed to look happy. You look upset, not happy, Stanley."

Stanley tried hard to smile.

Mr. Dart left and Stanley was alone.

It was dark in the main hall. A little bit of moonlight came through the windows, and Stanley could just make out the world's most expensive painting on the other wall. He felt as though the bearded man with the violin was just waiting, as he was, for something to happen.

The moon went behind a cloud and then the main hall was very dark.

Cr-eee-eee-k . . .

The creaking sound came from right out in the center of the main hall and even as he heard it Stanley saw, in the same place, a tiny yellow glow of light.

The creaking came again and the glow got bigger. A trap door had opened in the floor and two men came up through it into the hall!

Stanley understood everything all at once: these must be the sneak thieves! They had a secret trap door into the museum from outside and that was why they had never been caught. And now, tonight, they were back to steal the most expensive painting in the world!

He held very still in his picture frame and listened to the sneak thieves.

"This is it, Max," said the first one. "This is where we art robbers pull our biggest job ever, while everybody else sleeps."

The sneak thieves put down their lantern and took the world's most expensive painting off the wall.

"What would we do to anyone who tried to catch us, Max?" the first man asked.

"We would tie him up, Luther. What else?" his friend replied.

That was enough to frighten Stanley, and he was even more frightened when Luther came over and stared at him.

"I thought sheep girls were supposed to smile, Max. This one looks scared," Luther said.

Just in time, Stanley managed to smile, sort of.

"You're crazy, Luther, she is smiling," Max said.

Stanley waited until the sneak thieves had turned back to the world's most expensive painting, and then he shouted in his loudest voice: "POLICE! POLICE! MR. DART! THE SNEAK THIEVES ARE HERE!"

The sneak thieves looked at each other. "Max," said the first one, very quietly, "I think I heard the sheep girl yell."

"I think I did too," said Max. "Oh boy! Yelling pictures. We both need a rest."

"You'll get a rest, all right!" shouted Mr. Dart, rushing in with lots of guards and police officers behind him. "You'll get *ar-rested*, that's what!"

The sneak thieves were too mixed up by Mr. Dart's joke and too frightened by the police officers and guards to put up a fight. Before they knew it, they had been led away to jail.

The next morning Stanley Lambchop got a medal, and the day after that his picture was in all the newspapers.

For a while Stanley Lambchop was famous. But after a few weeks people forgot all about him. Stanley did not mind. Being famous had been fun, but enough was enough.

Later that night Arthur Lambchop was awakened by the sound of crying.

"Are you okay?" he asked Stanley.

Stanley waited for a long time before he spoke and then said, "I'm just not happy any more. I'm tired of being flat. I want to be like other people again."

"Oh, Stanley," Arthur said. And then suddenly he had an idea. He jumped up and turned on the light and ran to the big toy box. He found his old bicycle pump and said, "This is just the thing to pump some air into you and make you round again."

"Okay," Stanley said, "but take it easy."

"I'll go slowly," Arthur said, "and if it hurts or anything, wiggle your hand."

He began to pump, and at first nothing happened except that Stanley's cheeks bulged a bit. Arthur watched his hand, but there was no wiggle, so he pumped on. Then suddenly Stanley started puffing up.

Stanley spread his arms and gave them a quick wiggle so that the air could get around inside of him more easily. He got bigger and bigger. A moment more and he was all rounded out.

"Thank you, Arthur," Stanley said.

The brothers were shaking hands when Mr. and Mrs. Lambchop came into the room.

"GEORGE!" shouted Mrs. Lambchop. "Stanley's *round* again!"

Everyone was very excited and happy, of course. Mr. and Mrs. Lambchop tucked the boys back into their beds and kissed them, and then they turned out the light. "Good night," they said.

"Good night," said Stanley and Arthur.

It had been a long day, and very soon all the Lambchops were asleep.

Answer these questions.

1. What disguise did Stanley wear while he stood in the picture frame?
2. Why had the thieves never been caught?
3. What kind of rest did Mr. Dart say the thieves would get?
4. Why did Mr. and Mrs. Lambchop come into Stanley and Arthur's room?

Write on your own.

Pretend that you are flat like Stanley was. Write a few sentences telling why it might be fun.

How I Got My Ten-Speed Bike

New Words

1. The rain-soaked field looked like a <u>swamp</u>.
2. We walked to the <u>southern</u> part of town.
3. We planned to meet beside the <u>statue</u> in the park.
4. <u>Robbie</u> is my best friend.
5. We saw a <u>waterfall</u> high in the mountains.
6. We walked <u>twenty-five</u> paces from the tree.
7. We saw the <u>tigers</u> at the zoo.
8. <u>Petrified</u> wood is as hard as a stone.
9. Jim got six good books from the <u>library</u>.

How I Got My Ten-Speed Bike

John Griffith

I can explain how I got my new ten-speed bike. The map is what started the whole thing, and I can't explain *that* at all. I don't know to this day where it came from or who made it or how it got to where it was when I found it on our front sidewalk.

It was a beautiful sunny day, and I was going to my favorite friend Robbie's house. I didn't even notice the paper on the sidewalk until the wind picked it up and blew it in my face.

That caught my attention, so I grabbed the paper and looked at it. It was a *treasure* map!

Robbie laughed when she saw the map. "Treasure map? Do you really think this will lead to a treasure?"

"Well, I don't know for sure," I said, "but let's follow it and see if there is a treasure."

Robbie took the map, looked at it closer, and said, "Please explain to me how we are going to follow it, because these places on the map aren't around here."

"They're not?" I took the map back and said, "Well, it says to start at the southern tip of The Swamp."

"What swamp? We're in the middle of a huge city."

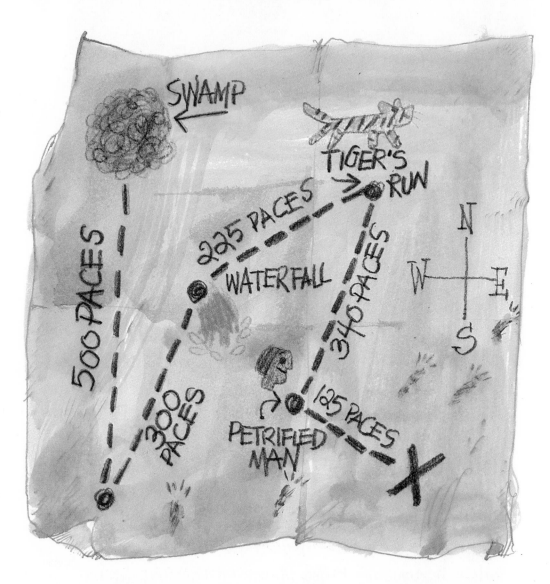

"What about down on Miles Street where they dug up the street and haven't paved it over yet? Since it's rained and that hole has water in it, that could be a swamp, couldn't it?"

"Yes, well maybe you could call it a swamp," said Robbie.

"Let's start there at the southern tip," I said.

So we did. We found the southern tip of the big mud puddle and then we started stepping off five hundred paces south, just like the map said.

"This is really silly," Robbie said.

We took three hundred steps northeast, like the map said, and landed in front of the library.

"The map says 'Waterfall,'" Robbie pointed out, "but do you see a waterfall in front of the library?"

I didn't.

We looked at the map together. "What about the fountain?" I asked. "There's a fountain in front of the library, and a fountain is almost like a waterfall."

"You're sure working hard to make that map come true," Robbie said.

"The next part says that two hundred and twenty-five paces from here is 'Tiger's Run,'" she said. "The only tigers in this town are in the zoo, and that's ten miles from here."

We took the two hundred and twenty-five steps anyway, and that put us just at the edge of the school yard behind George Washington High School. I was hoping maybe some kind of a striped cat might walk by.

"Look out, you kids! Come on, Tigers—move out!" shouted a voice from behind us.

Robbie and I jumped to the side as the high school football team went running to its practice field.

Robbie and I looked at each other.

"Running Tigers," I said.

"The Petrified Man," Robbie said as she looked at the map again. "What do you think *that* will turn out to be?"

We ran the three hundred and forty steps and almost bumped into the statue of George Washington that stands out in front of the high school. We didn't say anything for a while; we just stared at the statue.

"Petrified man," I finally said. "That would mean a man who had turned to stone."

"That statue is made of metal, isn't it?"

"What's the big difference?" I asked her.

She shook her head and said, "Okay, a petrified man. I wonder what we'll find a hundred and twenty-five paces southeast of here, where the big *X* is."

We counted off the steps and found ourselves in the park across the street from the school. We stopped under a large fir tree.

"Look at this!" I shouted. "Someone's already been digging."

In between the roots of the fir tree was a hole in the ground like chipmunks or ground squirrels make. Robbie and I got down on our hands and knees and looked inside.

"Robbie, there's something in there!" I yelled. "Come on, let's get a stick and dig."

She was just as excited as I was, and we both grabbed sticks and dug.

I must say that the treasure we found was pretty strange for a treasure; but you'll never get me to say that it wasn't a real treasure.

About three feet down that hole was a whole lot of bright, shiny stuff. A lot of it wasn't worth much—bottle caps and some glass from broken bottles. But there was some really good stuff there, too. We found nickels, dimes, and quarters worth over a dollar, and we also found a man's ring, made of real gold.

We did everything we were supposed to do about looking for the owner of the ring. We put an ad in the paper, and we told the police, but no one tried to claim it.

We sold the ring for three hundred dollars, then Robbie and I divided the money.

I spent my one hundred and fifty dollars on a brand new ten-speed bike. Robbie already had a bike, so she's spending her share a little at a time.

My dad says that the treasure we found was a pack rat's nest.

But where did the map come from? Pack rats don't make treasure maps, do they?

It's kind of funny though. Some of the marks on the map do look a little like paw prints. . . .

Answer these questions.

1. What did the girl find on the front sidewalk?

2. Why did Robbie say they couldn't follow the map?

3. How is a fountain like a waterfall?

4. What were some of the things they found in the hole?

5. What did some of the marks on the map look like?

Write on your own.

The pack rat came back to the hole and found that the treasure was missing. Write what the pack rat said about the missing treasure.

Footprints

It was snowing
Last night,
And today
I can see who came
This way.

A dog ran lightly here,
And a cat.
A rabbit hopped by and—
What was THAT?

A twelve-toed foot
Two yards wide?
Another step here
In just one stride?

It was snowing
Last night.
Who came past?
I'll never be knowing
For I am going
The OTHER way,
Fast.

Lilian Moore

The Boy Who Liked to Whittle

New Words

1. He stood on the <u>ridge</u> of the hill.
2. <u>Young Eagle</u> could run as fast as the wind.
3. The <u>ceremony</u> was very beautiful.
4. The <u>pheasant</u> flew out of the tall grass.
5. Large <u>buffalo</u> herds once roamed the central plains.
6. I use a <u>whittling</u> knife to carve.
7. He gathered <u>chalkstone</u> from the riverbanks.
8. He is a <u>Sioux</u> Indian.
9. My father said the <u>prayer</u>.
10. She asked me to <u>design</u> a new cover for the book.

The Boy Who Liked to Whittle

Frances Altman

Young James Fraser opened the door of the boxcar, which had been made into a home for his family. He looked over the peaceful green and purple hills until he spotted his friend, Young Eagle.

"I'm coming!" Jim shouted to the Sioux Indian boy, who was on the ridge of the hill.

Jim brushed his hat against his leg to shake off the dust and then smiled at Young Eagle. "How far is it to this ceremony?" Jim asked.

"Across three hills," Young Eagle said. "We'll have to run as fast as the foxes if we want to get to the ceremony in time."

As they ran, they rushed by a pheasant hiding in the tall grass, and the beautiful pheasant flew up high into the air.

Finally, on the ridge of the third hill, Young Eagle stopped. They were at the place of the ceremony.

"There—see down there," he pointed.

Below, Jim saw a tall Indian brave go into a pit he had dug in the sand. Jim saw thick steam coming from the hole.

"Hot stones are put into the pit to make the steam," Young Eagle explained. "The brave is getting ready for prayer. Tonight he will go to the prayer hill," he went on, "and you'll be able to see him from your home."

That evening Jim called his father to the door of the boxcar. Far away, against the red and purple evening sky, the Sioux brave stood on the ridge of the hill and reached up to the sky. That was how he stayed until the sun rose at his back.

"His prayer is for the return of the buffalo herds," Jim said. He told his father everything Young Eagle had told him. "Did you ever see a man look so lonely?" Jim asked.

"No," said Mr. Fraser. "You, James, have seen how the hunters have killed off the buffalo."

Jim understood why his Indian friends were often so sad when they thought of the buffalo.

The next morning Jim went into town with his father. Their town in South Dakota was small, but it was a railroad stop, and even early in the morning it was busy.

"It looks like I'll be busy at the railroad office for an hour or more," Mr. Fraser explained, "so take this money and see what you can find to buy for yourself."

Jim walked slowly along the wooden walk, studying every window. There were so many things to buy that he made his way from store to store, trying not to spend his money too quickly.

In front of one store Jim saw a man sitting on a bench on the porch. He saw that in one hand the man held a soft white stone and in the other hand he held a sharp whittling knife.

"You like to whittle?" the man asked.

"I enjoy drawing," Jim said. He watched the man finish his carving, then said, "I never knew you could whittle on anything but wood. I would like to learn to whittle."

The man held up his work so Jim could get a closer look, and Jim was surprised to see that it was a small cage with a round ball inside.

Carefully Jim took the soft carved stone.

"Could I whittle one of these?" he asked. "Would you sell me a thick piece of that stone to carve?"

The man laughed and said, "You don't need to buy it. Go down to Jim River, and you'll find chalkstone all over the riverbank. I'll sell you a good whittling knife, though—that's the secret."

As Jim hurried back to the railroad office, he thought of the Jim River and the chalkstone there.

From the riverbank of the Jim River the boy carried back thick pieces of the soft white chalkstone, and from then on, Jim spent every spare moment whittling.

The first thing Jim tried to carve was a cage with a ball inside, but he soon knew that the man could whittle far better than he thought.

Jim could easily carve a horse or a mountain goat in the stone, because he saw these animals almost every day. Sometimes he hid in the tall grass like a pheasant. He would watch small herds of buffalo eating, and these great animals soon became one of Jim's favorite things to draw and carve.

Carving in chalkstone as he learned the ways of the Sioux—that was how James E. Fraser, one of America's great sculptors, got his start. Today his work is found all over the United States.

Many years after Jim had become a famous sculptor, he was asked by the United States government to design a new nickel. He remembered his first friends in South Dakota and put the design of an Indian head and a buffalo on the nickel. In so doing, he made a nickel that was truly a design from America's past.

Answer these questions.

1. Where did Jim live when he was a boy?

2. What did Jim buy with the money his father gave him?

3. What kind of stone did Jim use for his carving and where did he get it?

4. Why did Jim put an Indian head and a buffalo on the nickel he designed?

The Flower-fed Buffaloes

The flower-fed buffaloes of the spring
In the days of long ago,
Ranged where the locomotives sing
And the prairie flowers lie low:—
The tossing, blooming, perfumed grass
Is swept away by the wheat,
Wheels and wheels and wheels spin by
In the spring that still is sweet.
But the flower-fed buffaloes of the spring
Left us, long ago.
They gore no more, they bellow no more,
They trundle around the hills no more:—
With the Blackfeet, lying low,
With the Pawnees, lying low,
Lying low.

Vachel Lindsay

Words to Know for Playing Games

Most of us like to play games. Before we can play a new game, we may need to read about it. These are words that help us understand new games.

directions   rules
equipment   object
partner   opponent
scorekeeper   continue

Choose the correct word for each meaning and write it on your paper.

partner directions
object opponent

1. the guidelines for the game
2. the person playing with you
3. the person playing against you
4. the goal of the game

equipment continue
rules scorekeeper

5. the person keeping score
6. keep on playing
7. the laws of the game
8. the things you need for the game

MYSTERIES

Gabrielle and Selena

New Words

1. <u>Goodness</u>! This room is a mess!
2. This fresh <u>pineapple</u> is delicious.
3. Do you <u>expect</u> to win the prize?
4. We will eat <u>dessert</u> after dinner.
5. The show will start at <u>seven-thirty</u>.
6. The dog sat <u>beneath</u> the table.
7. <u>Gabrielle</u> lives next door to me.
8. <u>Selena</u> came to visit us yesterday.
9. "Ugh!" said William. "I don't like to swim in cold water!"
10. We ate an <u>omelet</u> made from fresh eggs.

Gabrielle and Selena

Peter Desbarats

Gabrielle and Selena went everywhere and did everything together. Neither of them could remember a time when they hadn't been together. They were just like sisters.

Gabrielle seemed to know what Selena was thinking; and sometimes Selena would know what Gabrielle was going to say even before she said it.

Gabrielle had long straight hair that was almost blond and hazel eyes. Often she was quiet, but she wasn't *always* quiet.

Selena had short curly black hair and large brown eyes.

Although Selena could do many things well, her favorite thing and the thing she did best and most often was laughing. However, *sometimes* she was quiet, too.

One sunny day, when they were sitting on the front porch of Mr. Cox's building, halfway between Gabrielle's house and Selena's house, Gabrielle said, "Sometimes I wish, Selena, that I were you."

"Why do you want to be me?" asked Selena.

"I'm tired of being myself," Gabrielle said. "Every morning I wake up in the same bedroom, look at the same sister, say hi to the same dad and mom, brush with the same toothbrush, and eat the same meal for breakfast. Every day I do all these ordinary things, and I'm tired of them. I think it would be more interesting to live at your house."

"It's the same at my house," said Selena. "I always wake up in the same room and look at the same brother and eat the same toast for breakfast and do almost the same things that you do every day."

"But it's impossible that you'd do them *exactly* the same," said Gabrielle. "Wouldn't it be wonderful if we could trade places?"

"That's silly," said Selena.

"No it isn't," said Gabrielle. "All we have to do is press our hands together, like this, and put one foot touching the other foot, and put our noses together, and I'll gaze into your eyes, like this. Now we spin around twice, and then I say—'I am Selena.'"

"And I say—'I am Gabrielle,'" said Selena.

They each took two steps backward and stared at each other.

"Hi, Gabrielle," said Gabrielle.

"Hi, Selena," said Selena.

"Well," said Gabrielle, "it's almost time for supper. Good-by, Gabrielle, and enjoy eating dinner at my house tonight—I mean, *your* house."

"Good-by, Selena," said Selena, "and I hope you remember to feed my hamsters—I mean, *your* hamsters."

When Gabrielle arrived at Selena's house, she rang the doorbell. Selena's mom opened the door and said, "Hello, Gabrielle."

"I'm not Gabrielle," said Gabrielle, "I'm Selena."

"Oh, I see," said Selena's mom. "Well, Selena, I don't understand why you rang the doorbell, because Selena always just walks in."

"I just forgot," said Gabrielle.

Selena's little brother was in the living room, working a puzzle. "Hi, Gabrielle," he said.

"I'm Selena," said Gabrielle.

"Okay," he said, "but you sure look like someone named Gabrielle, Selena."

Selena's mom came into the living room and said, "Wash your hands, Selena, because it's time for supper and we're having your favorite vegetable—turnips."

"Turnips are my favorite vegetable?" asked Gabrielle, who couldn't stand them.

"Yes, they are," said Selena's mom, "and you always expect two huge helpings."

"Ugh!" said Gabrielle to herself.

When Selena arrived at Gabrielle's house, she walked right in, went into the kitchen, and said, "What's for supper?"

"Oh," said Gabrielle's mom, "are you going to eat with us tonight, Selena?"

"Of course I am," said Selena, "and my name's Gabrielle."

Gabrielle's mom set the skillet on the stove and asked, "Where's Gabrielle—I mean, where's Selena?"

"Selena's at my house—I mean, *her* house," said Selena.

"Very well, Gabrielle," said Gabrielle's mom, "you'd better wash your hands for supper. We're having your favorite meal—a delicious cheese omelet."

"That's my favorite meal?" asked Selena.

"You always expect an extra-big helping, too," said Gabrielle's mom.

"Ugh!" said Selena to herself, because if there was one thing she couldn't stand, it was a cheese omelet.

Somehow Selena ate most of her supper. When it was time for dessert, there were baked apples for Gabrielle's mom, Gabrielle's dad, and Gabrielle's little sister, and hot bread for Selena.

"Where's my baked apple?" said Selena.

"Why, Gabrielle, you know you never eat baked apples," said Gabrielle's mom. "You always expect bread and butter for dessert. Although we offer you dessert, you always say that your favorite dessert is bread and butter."

"I do?" said Selena.

When Gabrielle had eaten most of her turnips, trying to look as if she enjoyed them, Selena's dad said, "Now it's time to clear the table and do the dishes, Selena."

"But I haven't had any dessert," complained Gabrielle.

"Why, you know we always have fresh pineapple for dessert on Tuesday, and you don't eat fresh pineapple," said Selena's dad.

"I don't?" said Gabrielle.

"Never!" said Selena's dad. "You haven't had fresh pineapple since it made you ill."

"I'd like to try some tonight, however," said Gabrielle.

"I don't think that's a very good idea," said Selena's dad, "because if it made you sick, you couldn't wash the dishes."

"Wash the dishes?" said Gabrielle. "But I always watch television after supper."

"I don't know what you're talking about, Selena," said Selena's mom. "You never watch television because you always say you enjoy washing the dishes so much more."

At Gabrielle's house, Selena was sweeping the kitchen floor because Gabrielle's mom had said that this was her favorite thing to do before she went to bed at seven-thirty.

"You're saying that *I* have to go to bed at seven-thirty?" groaned Selena.

"No, you don't *have* to, you *want* to," said Gabrielle's mom. "Although I ask you to watch television with me, you say that it's healthy to go to bed early."

"Goodness!" said Selena to herself. "No wonder Gabrielle wanted to be me—omelets, sweeping the kitchen, going to bed at seven-thirty, and no television. This is a terrible way to live."

At Selena's house, Gabrielle had just finished the dishes when Selena's dad said, "Time for bed, Selena."

"But it's only seven-thirty," said Gabrielle.

"Is it that late?" said Selena's dad. "My goodness, by this time you're almost always sound asleep on the back porch."

"The *back porch?*" said Gabrielle.

"You're always saying that it's healthy to sleep outside," said Selena's dad.

"But it's dark out there, and probably freezing," said Gabrielle.

"I know," said Selena's dad, "but you always say that you would rather sleep on the cold back porch and gaze at the moon than be warm in an ordinary bedroom."

"Goodness!" said Gabrielle to herself. "I wish I'd known that Selena was such a nut—turnips, washing the dishes, and sleeping on the back porch."

Gabrielle stared at Selena's dad and said, "I'm going home."

"Okay," said Selena's dad, smiling. "Good night, Gabrielle."

Gabrielle and Selena met on the sidewalk below the streetlight in front of Mr. Cox's building.

"Hi, Selena," said Selena, looking at Gabrielle.

"Never mind calling me Selena," said Gabrielle, "because I wouldn't be you for all the money in the world. You didn't tell me that turnips were your favorite vegetable."

"Turnips?" said Selena, "I've never liked turnips. But you didn't tell me that you loved cheese omelets."

"Ugh!" said Gabrielle. "I hate cheese omelets almost as much as I hate washing dishes."

"Well, you sweep the kitchen floor every night," said Selena.

"I do not," said Gabrielle, "and at least I don't freeze sleeping on the back porch."

"Who sleeps on the back porch?" shouted Selena.

"But your dad said . . ." said Gabrielle.

"And your mom said . . ." said Selena.

Suddenly the two girls looked at each other and started to laugh, and their laughter sounded like silver bells beneath the streetlight beneath the moon beneath the soft black sky.

Answer these questions.

1. What did Selena's mom say Selena's favorite vegetable was?

2. What did Gabrielle's mom say Gabrielle's favorite supper was?

3. Where did Selena's dad say that Selena always slept?

4. At the end of the story, why did Gabrielle and Selena start to laugh?

Gift from Earth

New Words

1. That group is the <u>committee</u> from our class.
2. Those round flowers look like <u>pompons</u>.
3. We need to buy <u>supplies</u> for our hiking trip.
4. They will <u>request</u> that you help plan for the trip.
5. The <u>purpose</u> of our trip was to visit the museum.
6. Step <u>forward</u> so I can see you.
7. My new friend's name is <u>Novinia</u>.
8. A fishing pole is <u>essential</u> for a fishing trip.
9. I heard my favorite song on the <u>radio</u>.
10. Jill waited <u>impatiently</u> for her turn.

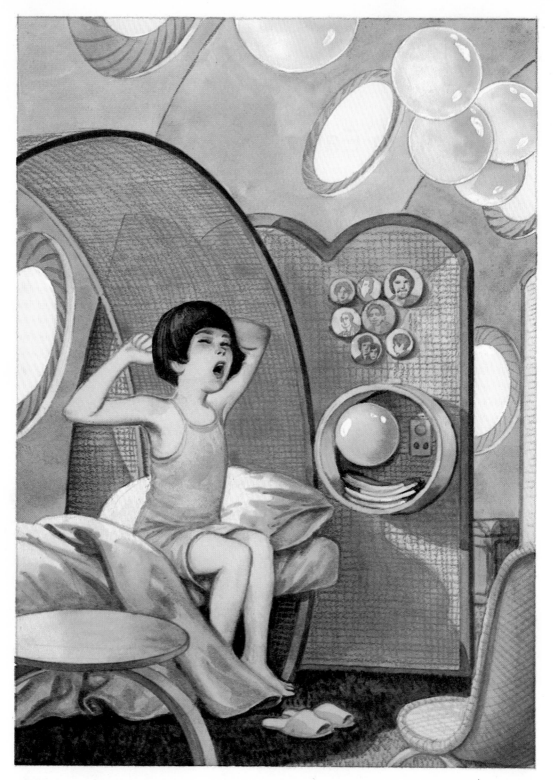

Gift
from Earth

Kathleen Pacini

Pale-yellow daylight came through the round windows of the plastic dome and woke Novinia. She sat for a few minutes on the edge of the bed, trying to remember why she was so excited. Suddenly she smiled as she remembered.

Today was the day the ship would come.

Today at last, after two years of waiting, the colonists on Dallas II would again see people from their home planet, Earth. The Earth people would tell about Earth and its way of life and would listen, fascinated, as the colonists told stories of life on their small planet.

Novinia wanted to hear everyone talk. Sometimes she could not believe that the stories her parents told her about Earth were true. But she was really waiting for what the Earth people would bring with them—the gifts.

When the colony on Dallas II was started, the colonists had to be happy with only things essential to life—soybean seeds, radio equipment, tools, hospital supplies, and hundreds of plastic-dome houses. Everything had been carefully worked out so that the colonists could live on the small planet. Over the years ships had come from Earth every so often, but there was only room for essential supplies such as radio and machine parts, tools, and extra hospital equipment.

But this time was different because there was a little extra space, and everyone on Dallas II could request special gifts. A committee talked about each request; the colonists wouldn't know until the ship came what the committee had decided to bring.

Again and again Novinia had thought about her own request. Would they be on the ship? Would the committee think they were useful enough to bring?

Her father had given her the idea. Ever since he had told her about the magic pompons he had played with as a child, Novinia had been fascinated.

"What were they used for?" she had asked him.

"Well, really nothing," her father had told her. "We just played with them. Some people thought they were a problem and had no purpose."

Novinia was puzzled and fascinated at the same time. She couldn't understand how there could be things that weren't useful. Everything on Dallas II had some purpose. Maybe that was why she wanted the magic pompons. The idea of having something that had no special purpose was as exciting as having the pompons.

She put on her new pale-yellow shirt and shorts and hurried into the kitchen of the dome, where her father was fixing soybean cakes for breakfast.

"Morning, Dad," she said. "Do you think it will come on time?"

"Will what come on time?" her father asked her.

"The ship!" Novinia said impatiently. Then she saw the laughter in his eyes, and she laughed and said, "Oh, Dad, no jokes!"

"I think it will," he said as he handed her some breakfast, "because the control tower called your mother to work very early this morning. As soon as you have finished, we'll go to the landing field."

"I'm finished now," Novinia said, pushing her soybean breakfast away. "Do you think they will bring my gift?"

"Don't count on it, Novinia," he replied, "because there isn't much room, and I'm afraid that what you want might be a problem. The committee may not think that your gift has a purpose on Dallas II."

"I know," she said, and sighed.

When they got to the control tower, many people were there. Novinia waved to her friends and to her mother. She could almost see her mother through the control-tower windows. Then she turned with everyone else to watch the sky.

Finally it came, a small point in the sky. Slowly, slowly, the ship came down to the landing field, and stopped. The ship from Earth had come, and Novinia watched, fascinated, as the door opened and the people came out. They smiled and waved.

"Will they give the gifts now?" Novinia asked her father impatiently.

Her father laughed and said, "Give them a few minutes. They need to get the supplies off first."

First came the hospital supplies and the tools and then the news from Earth on tape. Finally, when Novinia thought she could not bear to wait another second, it was time. The captain stepped forward, and Novinia listened to hear every word he said.

"You know we couldn't bring everything you wanted," he explained. "We could only bring the things that the committee talked about and felt were, in some way, essential for Dallas II."

Novinia waited impatiently as the captain began reading off each name and the people moved forward to get their gifts.

Suddenly all the boxes had been given out. Novinia should have known they wouldn't bring the pompons. Why had she requested something so silly?

Then the captain stepped forward again and said, "The committee talked about this last request for a long time. At first some people didn't think it was useful. But in the end they decided that Dallas II needs this gift just as much as it needs tools and radio equipment."

He pulled out a small plastic jar and lifted the lid.

In the dark dirt, twelve magic pompons grew on thin stems. One dandelion top was still yellow, but the rest of the puffs were round and white against the blue sky.

"They're more beautiful than I thought they would be," Novinia thought.

Then the wind blew across the landing field. The dandelion puffs lifted into the air, and hundreds of tiny dandelion seeds floated to their new homes.

Answer these questions.

1. Why was Novinia excited?

2. What had the ships from Earth always brought before?

3. What did Novinia request for her gift?

4. What did the captain have in the small plastic jar?

5. Why did the committee decide that the people on Dallas II needed the magic pompons just as much as the tools and radio equipment?

Write on your own.

Pretend you are a colonist on Dallas II. Write a short letter to the committee requesting something that you would like from Earth.

Dandelion Magic

Dandelions have a magic
All their own.
I'm not sure if it happens
Night or noon;
It's done so soon.
They give their golden yellow
To the sun;
They give their feathery whiteness
To the moon.

Leland B. Jacobs

Who Needs Plants?
We All Do!

New Words

1. Reading a good book gives me <u>pleasure</u>.
2. Apples and bananas are <u>natural</u> foods.
3. Those tall, tall trees are <u>redwood</u> trees.
4. This book will <u>provide</u> you hours of fun.

Who Needs Plants? We All Do!

Emilie Ferry

The world is full of plants. Plants grow in hot places, cold places, sunny places, shady places, and even underwater.

In some very cold parts of the earth, only a few different kinds of grass grow. But a hot rain forest is thick with plants that often climb all over each other, trying to find room to grow.

One kind of plant that grows underwater is so very tiny that two hundred of them in a row would only be one inch long. Other plants, like redwood trees, grow to be as tall as three hundred and fifty feet. Redwood trees are the tallest trees in the world.

Some plants live a long time. Some redwood trees are over one thousand years old, but they aren't as old as one kind of pine tree. The oldest of these pine trees is about five thousand years old. Other plants, however, live a very short time. There are some very small plants that live for less than an hour.

With so many plants in the world, most of us see them very often, and we sometimes forget how important they are. We couldn't live without plants.

Plants provide food for people and animals, and if all plants disappeared from Earth, we would run out of food very soon.

We eat all parts of plants. We eat the roots of carrots and the stems of celery. We eat the leaves of many plants. When we eat green onions, we're eating a part of the leaves. Some vegetables we eat are flowers, such as the cauliflower.

When we think of eating fruit, we may think of apples, bananas, peaches, and melons. But the part of any plant that holds the seed is a fruit. When we eat bread or any food made with flour, we are eating the fruit of different kinds of grass, such as wheat or oats. Even corn is the fruit of a very large grass.

Chickens, cows, and other animals eat food from plants, then the animals, in turn, provide us with food such as milk, eggs, and meat.

Plants provide many other things that we use, such as wax, cotton for clothes, and natural oil for soap. We use things made with wood from trees all the time. Many homes and other buildings are made with wood and some people even wear wooden shoes. Trees also provide paper for books and film for taking pictures.

Plants help us in other ways. They keep soil from washing or blowing away, and they keep the air fresh for us to breathe.

People get pleasure from plants. Everyone enjoys the shade of trees on a hot day. People who work with plants in a garden get pleasure from seeing natural things grow. And the natural beauty of plants gives us all a lot of pleasure, too.

Plants are wonderful things. We couldn't get along without them.

Answer these questions.

1. What kind of tree is the oldest and how old is it?

2. What parts of plants are eaten?

3. What things that we use do plants provide?

4. Why is it important that plants keep the air fresh?

The Mystery of Corbin Lodge

New Words

1. He had to <u>entwine</u> the rope around the pole.
2. We stayed at Ed's <u>Lodge</u> one night of our trip.
3. I invited <u>Elena</u> to my party.
4. I tried <u>desperately</u> to call you on the phone.
5. I want you to meet my friend <u>Juan</u>.
6. Here comes my sister <u>Celia</u>.
7. Let's give <u>Tomás</u> a ride in our car.
8. My uncle is named <u>Thaddeus</u>.
9. This gold watch is very <u>valuable</u>.

The Mystery of Corbin Lodge

Christine E. Scott

Elena sat up in bed suddenly; something strange had wakened her. She looked out the window beside her and saw the front yard below and a narrow strip of white sand by the lake. Everything was still in the moonlight.

Elena could hear the lake water lapping against the boats. Then there was another sound, a soft, crunching sound—like footsteps on sand.

The door behind her opened with a noisy squeak and Elena jumped. It was Juan. "Did you hear something?"

Elena nodded, and they peered out the window together. For a moment they saw a man walking along the water's edge; then he disappeared.

"He went toward the old Corbin Lodge!" Juan whispered.

Elena and her brother, Juan, had come to spend a few weeks at Stone Lake with Aunt Celia and Uncle Tomás. Around the bend in Stone Lake was an old weather-beaten two-story inn. They'd ask Uncle Tomás about it at the breakfast table.

The next morning, Juan and Elena talked excitedly about the man they'd seen the night before.

"Who do you think it was?" Elena asked.

"I don't know, but it's strange," said Uncle Tomás. "You'd better not go near Corbin Lodge; it hasn't been used for ten years."

"It's been empty since then?" Juan asked.

"As far as we know. Mrs. Corbin is the only one left of that family, and she now lives over by the store. Thaddeus Corbin was her husband's uncle."

"Thaddeus Corbin was strange," added Aunt Celia, "because he made up riddles all the time. He even left a riddle in his will about the lodge."

"It's said that after his death someone went into the lodge and never came out," said Uncle Tomás. "I know something's strange, because all the doors are hooked and locked from the inside, and people have heard closing doors and a clanging bell."

"Mrs. Corbin desperately needs money," Aunt Celia said. "If she can't sell the lodge soon, she may have to give up her home here. But she won't sell the lodge until the riddle's solved, because everyone thinks old Thaddeus hid something valuable there."

"Maybe it's a treasure!" Juan said. "What's the riddle he left in his will?"

"I'm going to see Mrs. Corbin tomorrow. Come along and we'll ask her," said Aunt Celia.

The next afternoon Aunt Celia, Juan, and Elena sat in Mrs. Corbin's living room.

"Elena and Juan have been hearing about the riddle in your uncle's will," Aunt Celia said. "Do you know any more about it?"

Mrs. Corbin sighed and said, "I've desperately tried to figure it out, but Uncle Thaddeus sure has me puzzled."

She went over to a desk, got out a tin box, and read from a small piece of paper:

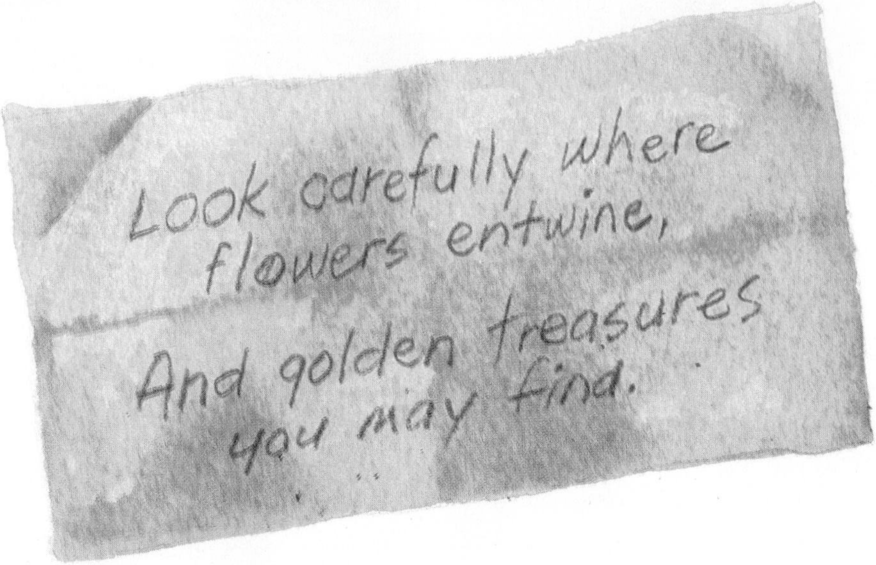

Look carefully where
flowers entwine,
And golden treasures
you may find.

"There was a small flower garden back of the lodge," said Mrs. Corbin, "but it's been searched and dug up a dozen times."

"Could we look around?" Juan asked.

"Look all you want, outside or inside the lodge, but just be careful!"

It was early the next afternoon when they began their search, and they started in the old flower garden.

" 'Where flowers entwine.' There's a vine of flowers on that gate, so let's start there," Juan said.

After searching for more than an hour, they decided to dig a hole.

After they had dug for an hour, Elena asked, "Do you suppose, Juan, the answer to the riddle is *inside* the lodge, not outside?"

They went up to the back porch and Elena tried to open the doors. "The doors are locked from the inside," she said.

They found an unlocked window, climbed in, and tiptoed through the empty rooms and up the creaking stairs.

At the top of the stairs there was a narrow hallway with rooms on each side. As they started down the hall, they heard a door close downstairs.

"A closing door!" they both gasped.

They went into the last room at the end of the hall and sensed something different. "Look! This room has wallpaper on the walls, and it looks like roses on the paper," said Elena. "Hey, roses are flowers! And look at this seam in the wallpaper where the flowers entwine!"

They put their fingers along the seam, and then Juan pulled the paper away to reveal a small wooden door. He opened it and pulled out a tin box matching Mrs. Corbin's.

Then there were footsteps outside the door, and in the doorway stood a tall dark figure—the man by the lake!

"I'll take that box!" the man said as he took a step forward and snatched the box from Juan's hand. "I figured a couple of smart kids might find it," he said. "Now come with me and be quiet."

He ordered them to walk in front of him, and all the way down the stairs Juan was trying desperately to think of something he could do.

Downstairs the man said, "Now don't try anything; hold hands and go into the garden."

The garden! Juan's heart leaped and he pressed Elena's hand, hoping she understood. It might be their only chance!

The man walked close behind them. In the growing darkness, and with his mind on his captives, he did not see the hole they had dug. Just as they approached it, Juan jerked Elena's arm, and they leaped to the side. The man took a step forward and stumbled into the hole!

"Run, Elena!" Juan shouted, as the man grabbed for Juan.

Then a big voice boomed, "Oh, no you don't!" It was Uncle Tomás, who grasped the man's coat collar tightly.

"Are you okay?" asked Uncle Tomás.

"Sure," Juan grinned.

"This is Sam Rogers, who used to work for Thaddeus Corbin. He must have been living in the lodge until he could find the valuable treasure."

After Sam was delivered to the sheriff, they went to get Aunt Celia; then they rushed to Mrs. Corbin's house.

"You found it in the lodge? Where was it?" asked Mrs. Corbin, as Juan gave her the box.

After Juan and Elena excitedly told the whole story, Mrs. Corbin lifted the lid of the box.

"Gold coins!" Juan exclaimed. "I'll bet they're valuable ones!"

"So this was Uncle Thaddeus's 'golden treasure,'" Mrs. Corbin said as she looked at Elena and Juan. "Thanks to you, I can stay here. Everyone must stay for supper!"

What an evening it was! As they ate the delicious meal, Juan and Elena felt they had never been so happy or so hungry before.

Answer these questions.

1. Why did Elena sit up in bed suddenly?

2. Why did Elena jump when the door behind her squeaked open?

3. Why did Uncle Tomás tell Juan and Elena not to go near Corbin Lodge?

4. What did the "golden treasure" allow Mrs. Corbin to do?

Words to Know for TV

Sometimes words are printed on your TV screen. These words help you understand what is happening. The words below are words you might see on a TV screen or in a TV guide.

Audio Trouble   Closed Captions

Please Stand By   Network Trouble

Weather Bulletin   News

Write the TV words that go with each question.

1. Which words let you know that a storm might be coming?

2. Which word tells you the important things that happened today?

3. Which words let you know that a deaf person will know what is being said?

4. Which words let you know something is wrong at the TV station?

5. Which words tell you there is trouble with the sound on the TV?

PROMISES

Cunningham's Rooster, Part 1

New Words

1. It seemed dark back in the <u>shadows</u>.
2. I named my new pet <u>Cunningham</u>.
3. May <u>Kenneth</u> eat supper with us?
4. We heard her play some <u>melodies</u> on the piano.
5. Our <u>rooster</u> crows every morning.
6. <u>Inspiration</u> is needed to paint a picture.
7. I <u>promise</u> not to tell your secret to anyone.
8. We have a picnic table on our <u>patio</u>.
9. He played a <u>rhapsody</u> on the piano.

Cunningham's Rooster

Barbara Brenner

Cunningham and Kenneth

There was once a cat named Cunningham who wrote music. That was his work. He made up songs for singing and songs for dancing and melodies just for listening.

First he would hear a song in his head, and then he would play it on the piano. After a while he would write down the notes in his big black notebook with a felt marker, so he wouldn't forget how the songs went.

They were wonderful songs, too. The only trouble was, nobody heard them, because Cunningham lived all alone except for his goldfish, and everyone knows that a goldfish has no ear for music.

It was beginning to get Cunningham down, and he hoped to find a friend who really enjoyed music.

"What good is a song if there's nobody around to hear it?" he asked himself.

One day as he sat playing the piano and wishing that a goldfish *did* have an ear for music, there was a pecking sound at the patio door. He looked up to see who it was and saw that it was a rooster.

"My name is Kenneth," the rooster said, as he opened the patio door with his beak. "I was walking by, and I stopped to tell you that I really like that song you're playing. It's so mellow."

Cunningham couldn't have been more pleased. "There's more where that came from," he said. "Why don't you step inside?"

Kenneth did step inside, and Cunningham played for him every song he had ever written—songs for singing and songs for dancing and melodies that were just for listening. When the music was over, Kenneth flapped his wings and clucked with pleasure. Cunningham knew then that he and the rooster were going to be good friends.

"Stay with me," he said to Kenneth, "and you can be the first one to hear my new melodies. You'll give me Inspiration."

"What's Inspiration?" Kenneth wanted to know.

"It's the feeling I get that makes me hear songs in my head," Cunningham explained.

"Well," said Kenneth, "I'll sure try to give you some Inspiration, but what will you give me?"

"A roost of your own and all the brown rice you can eat," said Cunningham.

"Agreed," said Kenneth quickly. "It will be a pleasure to stay with you!" He picked out a roost in Cunningham's bookcase and went to sleep, happy that he wasn't going to live in a barnyard anymore.

Having someone to listen to his music changed everything for Cunningham. Now every day found him happy and hard at work, making up songs and then writing them down in his big black notebook.

As for Kenneth, every day found him sitting under the piano, listening with pleasure to Cunningham's songs, or sitting on the piano, watching Cunningham writing notes down, or pecking and scratching around outside in the dirt, talking in riddles to the bugs before he ate them.

"Do bugs look like notes of music, or do notes of music look like bugs?" That was a favorite question Kenneth liked to ask.

One day Cunningham was watching Kenneth pecking and scratching in the dirt. Suddenly he shouted, "I have an Inspiration! I will make up some music about Kenneth. It will be a rhapsody and will have three parts to it. I will call it 'The Rooster Rhapsody'!"

He sat right down at the piano and began writing. The first part was all about Kenneth. It was about how Kenneth looked, the things Kenneth did, and what Kenneth was like. There were light sounds in it—like the way Kenneth clucked when he whispered to bugs and the cheerful little dance that Kenneth did when he was scratching in the dirt. It was a wonderful song, as light as feathers and as happy as the crow of a rooster in the morning.

When Kenneth heard the beginning of the rhapsody, he loved it.

"It's me all over!" he said.

Cunningham was pleased, too, because he knew it was by far the best music he had ever written. He decided to take it to the city and show it to an Important Music Person.

Before he left, Cunningham filled Kenneth's dish with brown rice and had a quiet little talk with him.

"Kenneth," he said, "I understand there's a hungry opossum who lives back in the woods. She has many teeth and would like nothing better than to eat a fat rooster. So promise me that you won't go out tonight after dark."

"Okay, I promise," said Kenneth.

All went well during the day, but as evening fell, fireflies began coming close to the patio door, and they winked at Kenneth from outside. The moon rose and made the trees look like shadows and the shadows look like trees.

The fireflies winked at Kenneth again and again, until he began feeling restless. He longed to talk in riddles to the fireflies and he wanted to visit his old barnyard friends.

At last Kenneth said, "This is the kind of night when a rooster could forget a promise."

He opened the patio door with his beak and took a step out into the dark night. Then he took another step and another.

He clucked softly to the fireflies, "Do bugs look like notes of music, or do notes of music look like . . . ?"

But before Kenneth had even gotten through the beginning of his riddle, the hungry opossum crept quietly out of the shadows, and suddenly . . . pounce!

Answer these questions.

1. What did Cunningham long for?

2. Who came to stay with Cunningham?

3. What did Kenneth give Cunningham that helped him write new songs?

4. Why was Kenneth happy not to have to live in the barnyard anymore?

5. What did Cunningham make Kenneth promise before he left for the city?

Cunningham's Rooster, Part 2

New Words

1. I was filled with <u>happiness</u> when I heard the good news.
2. We were filled with <u>sadness</u> after he left.
3. My birthday was a very <u>joyful</u> time.
4. She used a <u>flashlight</u> to see in the dark.
5. Thank you for the <u>lovely</u> flowers.
6. I couldn't <u>guess</u> what was in the box.
7. The circus is always <u>full</u> of surprises.

Cunningham's Rooster

The Rooster Rhapsody

Cunningham came home filled with happiness because the Important Music Person had liked his work and had said that it wouldn't be at all surprising if "The Rooster Rhapsody" made Cunningham famous. Cunningham couldn't wait to tell Kenneth.

But Kenneth couldn't be found.

Cunningham went to the kitchen and saw that the dish of brown rice was there, but Kenneth wasn't. He wasn't in the bookcase or under the piano or in any other favorite place.

Finally Cunningham took a flashlight and went out into the backyard. Cunningham could see from the light of the flashlight that there on the ground were the tracks of an opossum and four golden feathers from a rooster's tail. It didn't take long for Cunningham to guess what had happened. It was a sad cat who walked back into the house that night.

He put the flashlight away and sat down at the piano. He thought of all the good times that were over and all the sad years ahead.

Slowly Cunningham began to make up a new part to his rhapsody. Some of it sounded as restless as a spring night, some of it sounded like the pounce of an animal, and some of it was slow and low and full of the sadness of a lost friend.

"This is the second part of my 'Rooster Rhapsody,'" said Cunningham with tears in his eyes.

"I guess it is the last song I will ever write, because my Inspiration is gone, and what am I without my Inspiration?" he asked himself. "What's a cat without his work?"

Cunningham closed the piano and put away the big black notebook and the felt marker. Then he lay down on his bed and pulled the quilt over his head.

Those were terrible days, full of sadness. The milk went bad on the back porch, dust stood on the piano, and the goldfish bowl began to get dirty.

Then one morning there was a pecking at the patio door.

"Come in," whispered Cunningham, without even opening his eyes.

A moment later he heard a scratching sound, and the next thing he knew someone was pulling the quilt away from his head.

Cunningham opened his eyes, and there was Kenneth!

"Dear friend," cried Cunningham, "is it really you?"

"No one else," clucked Kenneth.

"I thought you were gone forever," said Cunningham. "I saw opossum tracks and rooster's feathers—"

"No, no, old friend," said Kenneth. "Remember—an opossum can pounce, but a rooster can roost! That's what I did—went up a tree and lost nothing but a few tail feathers."

"But why didn't you come back before now?" asked Cunningham.

"I guess I should have," Kenneth said, "but it was such a lovely spring night, and I wanted to visit some old friends in the barnyard."

Cunningham didn't have the heart to be angry with Kenneth. Also, at that moment, a new song came into his head. He blew the dust off the piano and began to play, while Kenneth cleaned the goldfish bowl.

What a wonderful song Cunningham wrote! A joyful song, full of mellow notes that were as golden as Kenneth's tail feathers. It was a lovely song about a friend who had come back and the happiness that had come with him, a song from the heart, a joyful song for everyone who ever had a friend and for everyone who ever loved music.

Now the three parts of "The Rooster Rhapsody" were finished. After Cunningham wrote down the last notes, he played the whole thing through . . .

The first part was joyful and as light as feathers, the second part was slow and low and filled with sadness, and the last part was lovely and mellow and golden.

Each song alone was fine, but all together they made the most beautiful music ever.

All the animals came out of the woods to hear "The Rooster Rhapsody." Soon the whole backyard was filled with animals, and every animal who heard the music went away filled with happiness.

As for Kenneth, he was so happy that he threw back his head and began to crow. Cunningham wrote down the sound of Kenneth's crowing, and it became the last notes of "The Rooster Rhapsody."

The rhapsody *did* make Cunningham famous. It made Kenneth famous, also, because every time "The Rooster Rhapsody" was played, someone would ask who had been the Inspiration for such wonderful music. Then someone else would always remember and tell the story of Cunningham's rooster.

Answer these questions.

1. What did Cunningham find when he went to look for Kenneth in the backyard?

2. How did Cunningham feel when Kenneth came back?

3. Where had Kenneth gone to get away from the opossum?

4. Why had Kenneth been gone so long?

5. What made Cunningham and Kenneth famous?

Benny's Flag

New Words

1. If you go outside, wear a <u>parka</u> to stay warm.
2. My friend <u>Benny</u> plays the violin.
3. The weather in <u>Alaska</u> can be very cold.
4. Alaska became a <u>state</u> in 1959.
5. Many children live in the <u>mission</u> home.
6. We went out with the <u>fisherman</u> to catch fish.
7. Did you win the <u>contest</u> and take first prize?

Benny's Flag

Phyllis Krasilovsky

Benny was an Indian boy who lived in Alaska many years before it became a state. Everyone liked Benny, for Benny liked everyone. He had many, many friends in the mission home where he lived. That was a place for boys and girls who had no families.

Benny was happy in the mission home. But sometimes before he went to sleep at night, he would look at the stars outside his window and long for the day when he would be a man. For then he was going to be a fine fisherman. He would use a big net like the Big Dipper to catch a big silver fish. And like the Big Dipper, which was really a great strong bear of night, he would be big and strong himself. The North Star would guide his boat, for the North Star is the star of Alaska, the most northerly state in America.

Sometimes, when the sky was scattered with hundreds of stars, it made Benny think of a field of forget-me-nots, the little star-shaped flowers which grow wild everywhere. The blue sky was a roof that covered Benny's Alaska at night.

In the summertime, when only the mountaintops were still covered with snow, Benny had fun going on picnics with the other mission children. Sometimes he went swimming, too, though the water was often cold.

One lucky day a fisherman took Benny fishing with him in his boat. Almost at once Benny caught a big silver fish all by himself. It was so big that there was enough for everyone at the mission house to eat for supper, and everyone said it was delicious.

Benny was so happy he could hardly sleep that night. He lay there looking at the stars, thinking of his dream of becoming a real fisherman. The Big Dipper looked more like a great strong bear than ever because Benny felt so big and strong himself!

When fall came, school started again. Then winter came quickly. The first snowy day Benny went to school wearing a parka, which is a fur-hooded jacket, and mukluks, which are fur-lined boots, and thick mittens to keep his fingers warm.

When Benny got to school, he hung up his parka and set his boots below it. That day the teacher told the children that there was a contest to make a flag for Alaska. With all his heart Benny wanted to win the contest. He thought how excited he would be to see his flag carried in a parade or hung on the mission-house flagpole on holidays or flying on the big ships that came to the village in the summertime. He thought how very special it would be to see his flag flying on the fishing boat he would have one day.

That night the boys and girls at the mission house collected crayons, paints, and paper, and made many, many designs for the flag. They sat around a big table and as they worked they talked and laughed and sometimes held up their designs for the others to see. But Benny sat quietly, thinking and thinking. He was thinking of what he loved the most about Alaska.

Suddenly Benny knew what he wanted his flag to be like. He wanted his flag to be like the stars he dreamed by—gold stars spread out like the Big Dipper in the blue sky. So that is what he painted. And below it he wrote: "The blue field is for the Alaska sky and the forget-me-not, an Alaskan flower. The North Star is for the future state of Alaska, the most northerly of the Union. The dipper is for the Great Bear—symbolizing strength."

Benny didn't show his paper to anyone. He was too shy. Still, the next day he gave his paper to the teacher when she collected the others.

Weeks and weeks went by and the teacher didn't say anything about the contest again. Benny went ice skating and threw snowballs with the other children. And so the winter went quickly by.

And suddenly the snow and ice began to melt. Benny no longer wore his parka and mukluks and mittens. He began to watch for the forget-me-nots in the fields as he walked to school.

He watched the fishermen mend their nets for the coming fishing season. He watched the world change from white to green.

Then, one day, when school was almost over, the teacher called the children together. "Children," she said, "the flag contest is ended. From all over Alaska boys and girls sent in designs for the flag, and *Benny's* design won the contest! From now on, *Benny's* design will be Alaska's flag!"

What a proud and happy boy Benny was! And what a very proud and happy boy he was on July 4th. For on that day there was a big parade in the village. Everyone came to see the parade. And the very first thing they saw was Benny at the head of the parade, carrying the flag he had made for the fishing boat he would have, carrying the flag he had made for Alaska!

Answer these questions.

1. Where did Benny live?
2. What did Benny want to be when he grew up?
3. Why were the children excited about the flag contest?
4. What things did Benny put on his flag?
5. Who won the flag contest?

Write on your own.

Design a flag for your state. Write a few sentences to tell what each figure stands for on your flag.

Do You Have the Time, Lydia?

New Words
1. We caught a <u>lobster</u> at the sea.
2. She needs a <u>ladder</u> to get up on the roof.
3. He raises plants in the <u>greenhouse</u>.
4. Did you finish your work or leave it <u>unfinished</u>?
5. The <u>sea gull</u> flew over the boat.
6. <u>Lydia</u> lives next door.
7. I am <u>sewing</u> a new dress for myself.
8. Hold the <u>steering</u> wheel with both hands.
9. Everyone must <u>obey</u> the rules.
10. I put my bike in the <u>garage</u>.

Do You Have the Time, Lydia?

Evaline Ness

Once there was a little girl named Lydia. She lived with her father, who was a florist, and Andy, who was her brother. Their house was on a tropical island in the middle of a warm and noisy sea.

Every day Lydia's father was busy in his greenhouse, where the plants and flowers grew so tall they needed holes in the roof to breathe.

Every day Lydia was busy painting pictures, reading books, gathering shells, sewing clothes, and making things. Lydia was so busy doing so *many* things, she left things unfinished—she never finished *anything.*

Andy didn't do anything because he didn't know how to. If he asked Lydia to help him do something, she always said: *No, no, no, no! I haven't got time!*

Whenever her father heard Lydia say: *No, no, no, no! I haven't got time!* he always said, "Oh no? Oh ho! If you *take* time you can *have* time."

But Lydia was too busy to listen and obey.

One bright and early morning, as Andy splashed along the beach, he found an empty lobster trap. He dragged it home and into Lydia's room, where she sat sewing a dress for the cat.

"Look," he shouted, "a racing car! Please, oh please, Lydia, fix it for me so I can be in the race Dr. Arnold is having. The prize is a dog!"

Without looking up, Lydia said, "No, no, no, no! I haven't got time!"

"The race is this afternoon!" begged Andy.

Lydia stopped sewing long enough to look at the lobster trap.

"Well, all right. I'll fix it—but later."

"You don't *care!*" cried Andy.

"I *said* I'd fix it, didn't I?"

Andy looked at Lydia for a long time, then he slowly left the room.

Lydia dropped the cat's dress. She found her roller skates and pulled them apart. She tied two wheels to each of the four corners of the trap. Then she cut two large circles of paper and taped them to the front for headlights. She took a small suitcase, dumped everything in it onto the floor, and placed it in the lobster trap for a seat.

"Perfect!" said Lydia. "All it needs is a steering wheel, and I know just where to find one!"

Lydia ran to the garage. In one corner, on a table, was a pile of junk. At the very top was a doll buggy with one wheel. She could use that for the steering wheel. As Lydia started to climb on the table, she noticed a large glass bowl on the floor.

"All *that* needs," muttered Lydia, "is a little water and a few tiny fish, and I know just where to find them!"

Lydia left the racing car unfinished and away she ran. She whizzed through the pine grove and down to the boathouse to get her fishing net.

The first thing she saw there was her father's small boat. It had water in it. Lydia tried to tip over the boat, but it wouldn't move. She found a rusty can in the boathouse and dipped out some water, but the more she dipped, the more water came in. Lydia threw the can away and fled up the beach to the greenhouse to tell her father.

When she was almost to the greenhouse, she stopped. At the edge of the water lay a gray sea gull. His eyes were closed and one wing was bent beneath him. Just as Lydia leaned over to touch him, he opened his eyes. Suddenly he shrieked and slapped her face with his good wing, so Lydia stepped back quickly.

"You need a doctor," shouted Lydia, "and I know just where to find one!"

She began to run. She ran so fast she had run out of breath by the time she reached Dr. Arnold's house, but Dr. Arnold wasn't home. Taped to the door was a note: BACK IN 10 MINUTES. JUDGING RACE.

The race!

Up the street flew Lydia. At the top of the hill she came to a sudden halt. There stood Andy, alone. The race was over. All the cars were at the bottom of the hill and Dr. Arnold was just giving a spotted dog to the winner.

Andy looked at Lydia with big tears in his eyes, then he turned and ran.

"Andy!" cried Lydia. "I was fixing it but I didn't have enough time!"

Andy kept running and he didn't look back.

Lydia watched him until he turned a corner, then she walked back to Dr. Arnold's house. She sat down on the steps and cried and cried. Then she stopped, because she had no tears left.

Suddenly a voice said, "Well! Have you finished your crying?"

Lydia looked down and saw Dr. Arnold's shoes, then she looked up and saw his face. "I guess I finally took time to finish *something*," Lydia said.

Dr. Arnold patted Lydia's head and asked, "*Now* what?"

Then Lydia remembered the sea gull.

"The sea gull!" she shouted. "Dr. Arnold! It's hurt. It's on the beach, and it can't fly!"

"Hurry!" she cried, when Dr. Arnold went into his office to get his little black bag.

"Hurry!" she called, as she ran ahead to the beach.

At last they were there, and there was the sea gull.

Very carefully Dr. Arnold worked a pill down the gull's throat to make it sleep, and then he taped its broken wing.

"This bird is going to be just fine," said Dr. Arnold, "but it won't be able to fly for a few days. Why don't you take the gull home, Lydia, and feed it a nice fat fish when it wakes up—that is, if you have enough time."

Lydia looked down at the sleeping sea gull and said, "Oh ho! I'll obey and *take* time!"

After Dr. Arnold left, Lydia carried the gull home.

She lined the bottom of a basket with seaweed, then she carefully put the gull on its cool wet bed.

Lydia went looking for Andy and found him under the porch.

Lydia brought the sea gull in its basket and placed it in front of Andy.

"Andy," said Lydia, "look what I found for you. The sea gull can be your pet until it gets well. If we obey Dr. Arnold's orders and take care of it and feed it fish, it will soon be well."

Andy looked at the gull, but he said nothing.

"Did you know that dogs can't fly?" asked Lydia.

Without looking at Lydia, Andy said, "I don't want your old bird."

Lydia left the sea gull with Andy and went back to the garage. She climbed on the table and pulled the wheel off the doll buggy. As she was leaving the garage, Lydia spotted a birdhouse that she had started to make a long time ago. All it needed was a roof.

"What that birdhouse needs . . ." began Lydia. She stopped and looked at the wheel in her hand, ". . . is *nothing!* No, I won't leave things unfinished anymore."

Lydia shot out of the garage and into the house to her room.

She had just finished fixing the steering wheel when a voice at her shoulder said: "I don't want your old trap."

"Oh, Andy!" cried Lydia. "Yes you do too! I'll paint it red and put a bell on it and give you my whistle and it will be a fire engine and you can go all around town and pretend to put out fires and rescue people!"

There was a long silence.

"Will it have a ladder?" asked Andy. "I would like a ladder."

"Yes, a ladder too! I promise! I promise!" said Lydia.

"But you don't have enough time," said Andy.

"Oh no? Oh ho! If I *take* time I can *have* time!" said Lydia.

Answer these questions.

1. Why did Lydia leave things unfinished?
2. What did Andy want Lydia to make from the lobster trap?
3. Why did Andy want to win the race?
4. Why did Lydia offer the sea gull to Andy?
5. What did Lydia promise to make for Andy?

Lengths
of Time

Time is peculiar
And hardly exact.
Though minutes are minutes,
You'll find for a fact
(As the older you get
And the bigger you grow)
That Time can
Hurrylikethis
Or plod,   plod,   slow.

Waiting for your dinner when you're hungry?
Down with the sniffles in your bed?
Notice how an hour crawls along and crawls along
Like a snail with his house upon his head.

But when you are starting
A game in the park,
It's morning,
It's noon,
And it's suddenly dark.
And hours like seconds
Rush blurringly by,
Whoosh!
Like a plane in the sky.

Phyllis McGinley

Words to Know to Read Signs

We see signs everywhere we go. It is important to know what these signs tell us.

Bus Station
Police Station
Construction Ahead
Handicapped Parking

Rest Rooms
Dead End
Speed Limit

These are places where you might see signs. Write these places on your paper. Beside each place, write or draw the sign you might see there.

1. on a building with buses outside

2. on a street which ends and does not continue

3. beside the street or highway

4. in a restaurant

5. in a parking lot

6. on the front of a building

7. in one lane of a street or road

JOURNEYS

Shingebis and the North Wind

New Words

1. He <u>murmured</u> his answer so I couldn't hear it.
2. The wind blew so hard, it sounded as if it <u>howled</u>.
3. I don't <u>dare</u> go outside in the cold weather without wearing a coat.
4. An Indian friend of mine is named <u>Shingebis</u>.
5. Indian Chief Songbird used to live in a <u>tepee</u>.
6. He was <u>determined</u> to get his work done early.
7. The <u>fierce</u> wind blew down a tree.

Shingebis and the North Wind

Sibyl Hancock

Fall was almost over, and all the Indians were getting themselves ready to travel south for the winter. All except one, that is.

"I'm not leaving!" young Shingebis exclaimed, looking very determined.

"But you must come with us," the Indians shouted, "because soon, when North Wind sweeps over the land, there will be no more fishing, and you will freeze!"

Shingebis shook his head, meaning this year he wouldn't flee to the warm south.

The Indians murmured among themselves. They agreed that Shingebis was brave, but to face North Wind was frightening.

"You'll be sorry," they said, "because all of your tricks will not help you this time."

"I will not leave," Shingebis replied in a very determined voice.

"North Wind is very strong," the Indians said, "and he uses his strength to blow the huge trees down before him."

Shingebis said, "I'm not worried, because during the day my leather clothes will keep me warm and at night I'll stay by the fire inside my tepee. North Wind won't dare to come inside!"

While everyone else got themselves ready to go, loading their canoes with the fish they had caught, Shingebis laughed and murmured to himself, "I'll show them that they shouldn't have to leave."

When the canoes were out of sight, Shingebis went to work. He tightened his tepee close to the ground, and began drying logs before the fire.

In the evening Shingebis sang before the fire and tried not to be lonesome. Each morning he went to the hole he'd cut in the frozen lake, and he caught many fish.

Cold days came, and North Wind howled. He drove all the little animals into their winter homes, he danced in the snowflakes, and trees moaned under his icy touch.

"Woo-oo-oo!" North Wind roared when he found Shingebis. "Who would dare to stay here long after the geese have flown? Who would dare to question my strength? Who thinks I am a gentle breeze?"

Great North Wind howled and stirred up cold, icy wind and made the snow drift so high that no creature would dare to travel about— except Shingebis. The young brave stepped right outside his tepee and went fishing.

North Wind said, "I'll freeze his fishing hole, and then Shingebis cannot eat!"

So North Wind roared and blew until the lake was covered deep with snow and the hole was frozen over. Determined, Shingebis did not give up, but moved on to another lake, cut another hole, and caught more fish.

"Shingebis must understand my strength!" North Wind howled.

However, each day Shingebis left his tepee to catch more fish, and each day the fierce North Wind couldn't stop him.

"Woo-oo-oo!" North Wind roared, "I'll blow down his door, then Shingebis will surely freeze!"

North Wind howled and roared outside the little tepee, but Shingebis just tossed more logs on his fire, and the wind's icy breath did not make him cold.

"You cannot beat me!" Shingebis shouted.

"I'll cause trouble until you freeze!" North Wind howled, and he slipped under the flap of the tepee.

Shingebis shivered, but he didn't say a word when the fierce North Wind sat beside him.

"I will freeze you!" North Wind howled, and he breathed his cold breath. Shingebis didn't look at the terrible North Wind as he reached forward to stir his fire. The fire leaped high, and its shadow played on the wall.

Suddenly North Wind's icy hair began to drip, then his face began to drip, and then his icy clothes began to drip. Fierce North Wind was melting!

Frightened North Wind howled, ran outside, and threw himself into a snowdrift.

"What a strange young man is this Shingebis!" he murmured. "I cannot freeze him; I haven't even frightened him! I think I shall leave him alone!"

North Wind didn't try to freeze Shingebis anymore. Sunny days came, and Shingebis watched as green buds appeared on trees and grass peeped through the melting snow. He no longer had to fish in a frozen lake, because the ice was melting.

Everyone else came back in their canoes at the first sign of spring. The surprised Indians were proud of Shingebis because he'd stopped the North Wind and had brought an early spring.

Answer these questions.

1. Who was the Indian that would not go south for the winter?

2. What did the other Indians say would happen to Shingebis if he stayed there?

3. What happened when North Wind came into the tepee and sat next to Shingebis?

4. Why couldn't the North Wind make Shingebis leave?

5. Why were the other Indians proud of Shingebis?

Write on your own.

Write what Shingebis did to get ready for winter. Tell what he did to stay warm and how he found food.

Pecos Bill Rides a Tornado

New Words

1. My favorite tree is the <u>cottonwood</u>.
2. The <u>tornado</u> came from the west.
3. He used a <u>lasso</u> to catch the horse.
4. The <u>valleys</u> were beautiful and green.
5. I live in the state of <u>Oklahoma</u>.
6. The <u>rattlesnake</u> moved slowly through the grass.
7. We crossed the <u>Pecos</u> River this morning.
8. The wind made a <u>roaring</u> noise.
9. We rode our horses <u>toward</u> the barn.

Pecos Bill Rides a Tornado

Wyatt Blassingame

Long ago in the Old West, cowboys were known to sing a ballad about a horse named Widow-Maker, who was so wild that nobody could ride him. Cowboys in Texas sang it while they tended their herds. However, one starry night a cowboy named Pecos Bill came riding across the prairie.

Pecos Bill heard the song and started to laugh. "I can ride any horse," he bragged to the other cowboys.

Then Pecos Bill took a huge leap and landed on Widow-Maker's back, and the wild horse began to buck. Widow-Maker spun like a top, backflipped, and went sidewinding up hills and down valleys, but he couldn't throw Pecos Bill. When Widow-Maker finally stopped bucking he was as tame as a lapdog, and he became Bill's favorite horse.

After that everybody agreed that Pecos Bill was the best cowboy in all the West. "Bill can ride anything with four hoofs and a hide," the other cowboys said, but nobody ever thought that Bill would someday ride a tornado.

This is the way that it happened.

One spring day Bill heard about a big storm that was roaring in from the west. Lightning flashed, thunder rolled, and the rain came down like a river standing on end.

Now about that same time, Bill watched another storm come up from the south that had winds blowing at one thousand and two miles an hour.

Suddenly, these two storms met head on and chased one another around and around until they turned themselves into the biggest tornado anybody had ever seen.

This huge tornado went roaring all over the West and picked up a thousand head of cattle on the Heart Bar Ranch in Texas and set them down nice as you please on the Crooked S Ranch in Arizona. Then it picked up the cattle on the Crooked S and set them down on the Bent W Ranch in Kansas. It picked up the state of Oklahoma and put it down in New Mexico, then it put New Mexico where Oklahoma had been.

All this was terrible enough, but the tornado made a mistake when it came roaring up the Pecos River in Texas, right past Pecos Bill's house.

Pecos Bill wasn't home when the twister passed because he was driving a herd of cattle to market, but he soon returned. "Whoa, Widow-Maker!" Pecos Bill shouted as he stopped to look around.

There stood Slue-Foot Sue, Bill's wife, but there wasn't any ranchhouse or barn. There weren't any cottonwood trees along the Pecos River—there wasn't even any Pecos River.

"Sue," Bill shouted, "what's happened around here? Where's our Pecos River?"

"The tornado took it," said Sue.

"Where's our house and barn and cottonwood trees?" Bill asked.

"The tornado took them, too," Sue said.

That made Pecos Bill really mad. "I've been driving cattle for a long time, and I'm hungry," he said. "Now I come home, and some crazy tornado has stolen my house—the kitchen and all. Which way did it go?"

"That way," Sue said as she pointed toward the west, "but you can't catch it because it's traveling a thousand and two miles an hour."

"Well, no tornado is going to take my house and get away with it!" shouted Bill as he rode off on Widow-Maker.

Bill galloped west straight across Texas. He was zipping over the mountains when he ran into a huge rattlesnake.

"You're in a mighty big hurry," the rattlesnake said.

"Did you see a tornado come past here?" Bill asked the snake.

"I did," the rattlesnake said, "but I won't tell you where it went unless you can make me, because I'm rough, and I'm tough, and I'm ready to fight."

Pecos Bill got down from Widow-Maker's back as he said, "Okay, but I'm in a hurry, so to make it a fair fight I'll give you the first three bites."

The rattlesnake bit Pecos Bill once and it turned pale and began to look ill. Then it bit Bill again and turned green, and the rattles on its tail started to fall off.

"That's enough—I don't want to fight anymore," the snake said. It pointed its head toward the north and said, "Your tornado went that way."

Bill jumped on Widow-Maker and galloped north. They galloped over more mountains and down valleys, and were racing through some high mountains when a huge cougar jumped down on the trail and said, "You're in a mighty big hurry."

"I'm chasing a tornado," Bill shouted. "Have you seen it?"

"I have," the cougar said.

"Which way did it go?" Bill asked.

"I won't tell unless you make me," the cougar said, "because I'm rough, and I'm tough, and I'm ready to fight."

"I don't have time to fight," Bill said as he leaned over, grabbed that cougar, and lifted him high off the ground.

"Set me down," yelled the wildcat, "and I'll tell you which way the tornado went."

Bill put the cougar down and asked, "Which way?"

"That way," the cougar said, "but I think I hear it coming back."

Sure enough, when Bill looked up, he saw the tornado roaring toward them. It was leapfrogging from one mountain to another, turning them upside down. It was turning rivers around so they would run upstream.

Quickly Bill took his lasso and began to spin it around and around his head until it was the longest lasso in the world. The noose got bigger and bigger, and the line got longer and longer as Bill swung it.

Then he let the noose go and it went up and up. It slipped along the bottom of the sky and over the top of the tornado.

Not even Pecos Bill could stop that tornado, but he held onto his lasso. It pulled him high in the air and swung him back and forth like the tail of a kite.

This didn't worry Bill, however. Hand over hand, he climbed up the lasso, swung himself on the tornado's back, and began to ride it like a wild horse.

"Whoopee!" Bill yelled, waving his hat with one hand. "Buck, you crazy tornado!"

Well, that tornado really went wild. It backflipped and turned head over heels and went sidewinding over mountains and down valleys, but it couldn't throw Pecos Bill.

Finally the twister began to get tired and it got weaker and weaker. Bill made it put the cattle back where they came from, and put Oklahoma and New Mexico back where they came from. Then he made it carry his house and his barn and the cottonwood trees and the Pecos River back to Texas.

By now the tornado was so tired, it just had
strength for one last bolt of lightning. Bill grabbed
the lightning bolt and slid down it to the ground.

Slue-Foot Sue and Widow-Maker were waiting
on the front porch of the ranchhouse.

"You've got our house and barn back," Sue
shouted, "but what took you so long?"

"Sue," Pecos Bill said, "I've been fighting with a rattlesnake and a cougar. I've been riding the tornado from Oklahoma to New Mexico to Texas. Now I'm as hungry as a bear."

"Well, come on in and we'll eat supper," said Sue.

While they were eating, Sue heard a noise outside and asked, "What's that?"

Bill looked out the window and said, "It's that tornado, but now it's as gentle as a spring breeze and playing in our backyard like a puppy."

"Well, let's keep it," Sue said, "because it'll be nice to have a breeze of our own when the weather gets hot this summer."

Answer these questions.

1. Who was the first person to ride Widow-Maker?

2. How did Pecos Bill tame Widow-Maker?

3. Why did Pecos Bill get mad at the tornado?

4. How fast did Slue-Foot Sue say the tornado was moving?

5. How did Pecos Bill get on the tornado to ride it?

6. How did Pecos Bill get from the tornado to the ground?

Daydreams

I flew like a bird through the clouds today
And took a rocket to Mars;
I knew the magic words to say
To a man who came from the stars.

I sailed like a whale on the ocean blue
To the land of dragons old,
And saved a friend from a pirate crew;
I was so brave and bold.

I put on my hat and climbed on my horse
And rode off into the West,
And when the cowboys mentioned my name,
They all said I was the best.

I ran like a deer through the jungle dark
To find the hidden gold,
And ended up in the city park
With a cure for the common cold.

I can be what I want to be,
It can snow in the middle of June,
And I can go wherever I please
And never leave the room.

Evan Marks

278

Grandma Moses

New Words

1. Her <u>daughter</u> lived next door.
2. I <u>bought</u> one of the paintings.
3. My aunt lives in <u>New York</u>.
4. I need a smaller <u>needle</u>.
5. She used her <u>imagination</u> to paint beautiful pictures.
6. She lived on a farm in <u>rural</u> America.
7. He <u>expressed</u> his thoughts very well.
8. <u>Mary</u> is my best friend.
9. She painted a beautiful <u>scene</u>.
10. We lived in <u>Albany</u> for two years.

"Grandma Moses Painting, 1952." Photo Ifor Thomas. Copyright ©1975, Grandma Moses Properties Co., New York.

Grandma Moses

Charles P. Graves

Anna Mary Moses enjoyed visiting her grown children. Once she was at the home of her daughter, Anna, when her daughter said, "Mother, I wish you'd make me a yarn picture. I saw one that was very pretty, but I know you could make a better one."

A yarn picture is a scene stitched with a needle onto a piece of cloth, using yarn of many different colors.

Anna Mary went to work and soon finished a beautiful yarn picture, which her daughter loved. Anna Mary liked making yarn pictures and made it her hobby.

However, as Anna Mary grew older, her fingers became stiff and hurt her when she tried to work with a needle.

"I enjoy keeping busy," she said to one of her sisters, "but my fingers hurt so much when I embroider with a needle."

"Wouldn't it be easier to hold a paint brush?" her sister said. "You used to paint—why not try that?"

"Why, that's a good idea," Anna Mary agreed.

So Anna Mary started to paint with real purpose. Before she began a picture, she would shut her eyes and use her imagination to create a scene from her childhood. Her pictures were set in rural America and had red barns and white houses, church steeples, miles and miles of snow, and lots of horses, cows, chickens, and children. Anna Mary loved people so much that she often put lots of them in her pictures. Her paintings expressed her feelings about her childhood.

Grandma Moses, *Joy Ride.* Copyright © 1982, Grandma Moses Properties Co., New York.

"I see the whole picture before I start to paint," she said. "It's all imagination; I paint what I remember."

Her son Hugh and his wife, Dorothy, were very excited about her new hobby. One day soon after her 77th birthday, they took some of the best paintings and put them in a drug store where everyone could see them.

A year later Dorothy told Anna Mary, "A man came to see you and he said he wants to buy *all* your pictures. He's already bought those at the drug store."

"That's exciting news," Anna Mary said. "What's the man's name?"

"Louis J. Caldor," Dorothy replied, "and he's coming back tomorrow to see your other paintings."

Early the next day Mr. Caldor came to see Anna Mary. She showed him her paintings, and he thought they were so wonderful that he bought them all.

A year later, in the fall of 1939, Anna Mary heard from Mr. Caldor that three of her paintings had been chosen for a showing at the Museum of Modern Art in New York. Anna Mary's paintings were hung in the museum for a month, but they did not receive much attention.

Grandma Moses, *Wash Day.* Copyright © 1979, Grandma Moses Properties Co., New York. From the collection of the Museum of Art, Rhode Island School of Design.

However, Anna Mary was still one of Mr. Caldor's favorite artists, so he bought more of her pictures to take back to New York.

After a time, Mr. Caldor showed some of Anna Mary's paintings to a man named Dr. Kallir, who agreed to show some of them in his art gallery.

Just after the showing opened, a story about Anna Mary appeared in a New York City newspaper. In the story, she was called "Grandma Moses" and soon everyone chose to call her by that name.

Slowly at first, and then faster and faster, people started to buy Grandma Moses' paintings. Millions of people fell in love with her pictures and they fell in love with Grandma Moses, too.

The people were pleased that a person who had never had an art lesson could start painting at age 76 and be a success. She was an inspiration to many elderly people who wanted to try painting, too.

In 1949 Grandma Moses was one of five people chosen to receive an award from a press club in Washington, D.C.

While she was in Washington, Grandma Moses was invited to be the guest of Mrs. Harry Truman, the wife of the president. During their visit, the president came in and sat down next to Grandma.

"You remind me of my mother," the president said.

Grandma Moses, *Taking Leg Bale for Security*. Copyright ©1975, Grandma Moses Properties Co., New York.

"Well," Grandma replied to the president, "you remind me of my sons."

The president and Grandma Moses talked about rural life on a farm.

"You talk like a good farmer," Grandma said, "and I understand that you are also a good piano player. Will you play something for me?"

The president went to the piano and played a song for her.

Grandma Moses became very famous. On her 90th birthday the mayor of Albany, New York, named the day "Grandma Moses Day." Albany is the capital of New York. That night Albany threw a huge birthday party for her.

Even after Grandma Moses became famous, she kept working as she had before, using her imagination to create new paintings. She did most of her painting in her bedroom on a flat work table.

Grandma started each day's painting early in the morning and most of the time she worked on many pictures at the same time.

"It saves paint," she explained. "I do the blue for one sky and then the other three skies, and I paint from the top down. First I paint the sky, then the mountains, then the hills, then the trees, the houses, the livestock, and the people."

Grandma Moses, *In the Park*. Copyright ©1986, Grandma Moses Properties Co., New York.

Grandma Moses was one hundred years old on September 7, 1960. Many reporters came to ask her questions on her birthday, and she expressed her feelings about living a long life.

"It's nothing to get that old," she said cheerfully. "You just tell a lot of bad stories, you laugh, and you'll get there yourself. It's as easy as that."

Then she said to everyone, "Painting is not important; the important thing is keeping busy."

Grandma Moses lived until December 13, 1961, when she was over 101 years old.

Grandma Moses, *Rainbow.* Copyright ©1982, Grandma Moses Properties Co., New York.

Grandma Moses called her last painting *Rainbow.* This scene, like so many that she had painted, expressed the simple joys of life in the rural America of long ago.

Answer these questions.

1. What did Anna Mary Moses do each time before she started to paint a picture?

2. Why did the newspaper call Anna Mary Moses "Grandma Moses"?

3. What did Grandma Moses say was more important than painting?

4. What did the scenes in Grandma Moses' paintings express?

The House at Pooh Corner, Part 1

New Words

1. I sat in an <u>arm-chair</u> to read my book.
2. The number after ten is <u>eleven</u>.
3. The new boy in our class <u>timidly</u> said hello.
4. I went to see my <u>relations</u>.
5. He didn't know which way to go and felt very <u>muddled</u>.
6. I put the dishes in the <u>cupboard</u>.
7. I <u>practised</u> my song on the piano.
8. Susan is <u>anxiously</u> waiting to go on vacation.
9. "The storm is getting worse," Mother said <u>solemnly</u>.
10. Katy and Amy want to <u>build</u> a clubhouse.

The
House
at
Pooh Corner

A. A. Milne

A Good Hum

One day when Pooh Bear had nothing else to do, he thought he would do something, so he went round to Piglet's house to see what Piglet was doing. It was still snowing as he stumped over the white forest track, and he expected to find Piglet warming his toes in front of his fire, but to his surprise he saw that the door was open, and the more he looked inside the more Piglet wasn't there.

"He's out," said Pooh sadly. "That's what it is. He's not in. I shall have to go a fast Thinking Walk by myself. Bother!"

But first he thought that he would knock very loudly just to make *quite* sure . . . and while he waited for Piglet not to answer, he jumped up and down to keep warm, and a hum came suddenly into his head, which seemed to him a Good Hum, such as is Hummed Hopefully to Others.

The more it snows
(Tiddely pom),
The more it goes
(Tiddely pom),
The more it goes
(Tiddely pom),
On snowing.
And nobody knows
(Tiddely pom),
How cold my toes
(Tiddely pom),
How cold my toes
(Tiddely pom),
Are growing.

"So what I'll do," said Pooh, "is I'll do this. I'll just go home first and see what the time is, and perhaps I'll put a muffler round my neck, and then I'll go and see Eeyore and sing it to him."

He hurried back to his own house; and his mind was so busy on the way with the hum that he was getting ready for Eeyore that, when he suddenly saw Piglet sitting in his best arm-chair, he could only stand there rubbing his head and wondering whose house he was in.

"Hallo, Piglet," he said. "I thought you were out."

"No," said Piglet, "it's you who were out, Pooh."

"So it was," said Pooh. "I knew one of us was."

He looked up at his clock, which had stopped at five minutes to eleven some weeks ago.

"Nearly eleven o'clock," said Pooh happily. "You're just in time for a little smackerel of something," and he put his head into the cupboard. "And then we'll go out, Piglet, and sing my song to Eeyore."

"Which song, Pooh?"

"The one we're going to sing to Eeyore," explained Pooh.

The clock was still saying five minutes to eleven when Pooh and Piglet set out on their way half an hour later. The wind had dropped, and the snow, tired of rushing round in circles trying to catch itself up, now fluttered gently down until it found a place on which to rest, and sometimes the place was Pooh's nose and sometimes it wasn't, and in a little while Piglet was wearing a white muffler round his neck and feeling more snowy behind the ears than he had ever felt before.

"Pooh," he said at last, and a little timidly, because he didn't want Pooh to think he was Giving In, "I was just wondering. How would it be if we went home now and *practised* your song, and then sang it to Eeyore to-morrow—or—or the next day, when we happen to see him."

"That's a very good idea, Piglet," said Pooh. "We'll practise it now as we go along. But it's no good going home to practise it, because it's a special Outdoor Song which Has To Be Sung In The Snow."

"Are you sure?" asked Piglet anxiously.

"Well, you'll see, Piglet, when you listen. Because this is how it begins. *The more it snows, tiddely pom—*"

"Tiddely what?" said Piglet.

"Pom," said Pooh. "I put that in to make it more hummy. *The more it goes, tiddely pom, the more—*"

"Didn't you say snows?"

"Yes, but that was *before.*"

"Before the tiddely pom?"

"It was a *different* tiddely pom," said Pooh, feeling rather muddled now. "I'll sing it to you properly and then you'll see."

So he sang it again.

> The more it
> SNOWS-tiddely-pom,
> The more it
> GOES-tiddely-pom
> The more it
> GOES-tiddely-pom
> On
> Snowing.
>
> And nobody
> KNOWS-tiddely-pom,
> How cold my
> TOES-tiddely pom
> How cold my
> TOES-tiddely-pom
> Are
> Growing.

He sang it like that, which is much the best
way of singing it, and when he had finished, he
waited for Piglet to say that, of all the Outdoor
Hums for Snowy Weather he had ever heard, this
was the best. And, after thinking the matter out
carefully, Piglet said:

"Pooh," he said solemnly, "it isn't the *toes* so
much as the *ears.*"

By this time they were getting near Eeyore's
Gloomy Place, which was where he lived, and as
it was still very snowy behind Piglet's ears, and
he was getting tired of it, they turned into a little
pine wood, and sat down on the gate which led
into it. They were out of the snow now, but it was
very cold, and to keep themselves warm they
sang Pooh's song right through six times, Piglet
doing the tiddely-poms and Pooh doing the rest
of it, and both of them thumping on the top of the
gate with pieces of stick at the proper places.
And in a little while they felt much warmer, and
were able to talk again.

"I've been thinking," said Pooh, "and what
I've been thinking is this. I've been thinking
about Eeyore."

"What about Eeyore?"

"Well, poor Eeyore has nowhere to live."

"Nor he has," said Piglet.

"*You* have a house, Piglet, and I have a house, and they are very good houses. And Christopher Robin has a house, and Owl and Kanga and Rabbit have houses, and even Rabbit's friends and relations have houses or somethings, but poor Eeyore has nothing. So what I've been thinking is: Let's build him a house."

"That," said Piglet, "is a Grand Idea. Where shall we build it?"

"We will build it here," said Pooh, "just by this wood, out of the wind, because this is where I thought of it. And we will call this Pooh Corner. And we will build an Eeyore House with sticks at Pooh Corner for Eeyore."

"There was a heap of sticks on the other side of the wood," said Piglet. "I saw them. Lots and lots. All piled up."

"Thank you, Piglet," said Pooh. "What you have just said will be a Great Help to us, and because of it I could call this place Poohanpiglet Corner if Pooh Corner didn't sound better, which it does, being smaller and more like a corner. Come along."

So they got down off the gate and went around to the other side of the wood to fetch the sticks.

Answer these questions.

1. To whom did Pooh want to sing his song?

2. Why didn't Pooh want to practice his song at home?

3. Why didn't Piglet say that Pooh's song was the best he had heard?

4. What did Pooh and Piglet want to build for Eeyore?

The House at Pooh Corner, Part 2

New Words

1. My shoes were <u>uncomfortable</u> because they were too small.
2. Grandma Moses was a <u>remarkable</u> woman.
3. The <u>icicles</u> melted when the sun came out.
4. "<u>Stuffy</u> and still," said Jenny, "is how the air feels."
5. My raincoat is <u>waterproof</u>.
6. She wore her <u>macintosh</u> out into the rain.
7. Please do not <u>complain</u> about the rainy weather.
8. The angry man talked with a <u>gruff</u> voice.
9. Bob <u>proudly</u> showed us the picture he had drawn.
10. "I can't go," Jim said in a <u>melancholy</u> voice.

The
House
at
Pooh Corner

Eeyore's House

Christopher Robin had spent the morning indoors going to Africa and back, and he had just got off the boat and was wondering what it was like outside, when who should come knocking at the door but Eeyore.

"Hallo, Eeyore," said Christopher Robin, as he opened the door and came out. "How are *you?*"

"It's snowing still," said Eeyore gloomily.

"So it is."

"And freezing."

"Is it?"

"Yes," said Eeyore. "However," he said, brightening up a little, "we haven't had an earthquake lately."

"What's the matter, Eeyore?"

"Nothing, Christopher Robin. Nothing important. I suppose you haven't seen a house or whatnot anywhere about?"

"What sort of a house?"

"Just a house."

"Who lives there?"

"I do. At least I thought I did. But I suppose I don't. After all, we can't all have houses."

"But, Eeyore, I didn't know—I always thought—"

"I don't know how it is, Christopher Robin, but what with all this snow and one thing and another, not to mention icicles and such-like, it isn't so Hot in my field about three o'clock in the morning as some people think it is. It isn't Close, if you know what I mean—not so as to be uncomfortable. It isn't Stuffy. In fact, Christopher Robin," he went on in a loud whisper, "quite-between-ourselves-and-don't-tell-anybody, it's Cold."

"Oh, Eeyore!"

"And I said to myself: The others will be sorry if I'm getting myself all cold. They haven't got Brains, any of them, only grey fluff that's blown into their heads by mistake, and they don't Think, but if it goes on snowing for another six weeks or so, one of them will begin to say to himself: 'Eeyore can't be so very much too Hot about three o'clock in the morning.' And then it will Get About. And they'll be Sorry."

"Oh, Eeyore!" said Christopher Robin, feeling very sorry already.

"I don't mean you, Christopher Robin. You're different. So what it all comes to is that I built myself a house down by my little wood."

"Did you really? How exciting!"

"The really exciting part," said Eeyore in his most melancholy voice, "is that when I left it this morning it was there, and when I came back it wasn't. Not at all, very natural, and it was only Eeyore's house. But still I just wondered."

Christopher Robin didn't stop to wonder. He was already back in *his* house, putting on his waterproof hat, his waterproof boots and his waterproof macintosh as fast as he could.

"We'll go and look for it at once," he called out to Eeyore.

"Sometimes," said Eeyore, "when people have quite finished taking a person's house, there are one or two bits which they don't want and are rather glad for the person to take back, if you know what I mean. So I thought if we just went—"

"Come on," said Christopher Robin, and off they hurried, and in a very little time they got to the corner of the field by the side of the pine-wood, where Eeyore's house wasn't any longer.

"There!" said Eeyore. "Not a stick of it left! Of course, I've still got all this snow to do what I like with. One mustn't complain."

But Christopher Robin wasn't listening to Eeyore, he was listening to something else.

"Can't you hear it?" he asked.

"What is it? Somebody laughing?"

"Listen."

They both listened . . . and they heard a deep gruff voice saying in a singing voice that the more it snowed the more it went on snowing and a small high voice tiddely-pomming in between.

"It's Pooh," said Christopher Robin excitedly. . . .

"Possibly," said Eeyore.

"*And* Piglet!" said Christopher Robin excitedly.

"Probably," said Eeyore. "What we *want* is a
Trained Bloodhound."

The words of the song changed suddenly.

"We've finished our HOUSE!" sang the gruff
voice.

"Tiddely pom!" sang the squeaky one.

"It's a beautiful HOUSE . . ."

"Tiddely pom . . ."

"I wish it were MINE. . . ."

"Tiddely pom. . . ."

They came round the corner, and there was
Eeyore's house, looking as comfy as anything.

"There you are," said Piglet.

"Inside as well as outside," said Pooh proudly.

Eeyore went inside . . . and came out again.

"It's a remarkable thing," he said. "It *is* my house, and I built it where I said I did, so the wind must have blown it here. And the wind blew it right over the wood, and blew it down here, and here it is as good as ever. In fact, better in places."

"Much better," said Pooh and Piglet together.

"It just shows what can be done by taking a little trouble," said Eeyore. "Do you see, Pooh? Do you see, Piglet? Brains first and then Hard Work. Look at it! *That's* the way to build a house," said Eeyore proudly.

So they left him in it; and Christopher Robin went back to lunch with his friends Pooh and Piglet, and on the way they told him of the Awful Mistake they had made. And when he had finished laughing, they all sang the Outdoor Song for Snowy Weather the rest of the way home, Piglet, who was still not quite sure of his voice, putting in the tiddely-poms again.

"And I know it *seems* easy," said Piglet to himself, "but it isn't *every one* who could do it."

Answer these questions.

1. How did Christopher Robin get to Africa and back in the morning?

2. What was Eeyore missing?

3. Who went with Eeyore to look for his house?

4. How did Eeyore say that his house moved to a new place?

Words to Know in Newspapers

These words are found as headings in newspapers. They help you know what is in each part of the newspaper.

Editorials   Business
Classified Ads   Weather
Entertainment   Sports
Television   Comics

Number your paper from 1 to 8. Read each group of words. Write the newspaper heading that matches the group of words.

1. Partly Cloudy and Cooler

2. Help Wanted

3. Computer Company Buys More Computers

4. Peanuts

5. Piano Concert Set for Thursday

6. Home Runs Help Braves Save Game

7. Prime Time Listings

8. Cleaner Air Is a Must

Glossary

Entries adapted from *The HBJ School Dictionary,* copyright © 1977, 1972, 1968 by Harcourt Brace Jovanovich, Inc., are reprinted by permission of the publisher.

Key to Pronunciation
Listed below are diacritical symbols and key words. The boldface letters in the key words represent the sounds indicated by the symbols.

/ā/	cake	/d/	**d**uck
/ă/	hat	/ē/	b**ea**n
/ä/	father	/ĕ/	p**e**t
/är/	car	/f/	**f**un
/âr/	care	/g/	**g**o
/b/	boy	/gz/	e**x**act
/ch/	church	/h/	**h**ome

/(h)w/	white	/ou/	out
/ī/	pie	/p/	pet
/ĭ/	pig	/r/	run
/ir/	dear	/s/	see
/j/	jump	/sh/	ship
/k/	kite	/t/	top
/ks/	box	/th/	thin
/kw/	quit	/th/	this
/l/	look	/ŭ/	nut
/m/	man	/ûr/	fur
/n/	not	/v/	vine
/ng/	sing	/w/	will
/ō/	rope	/y/	yes
/ŏ/	top	/yoo/	use
/ô/	saw	/z/	zoo
/oi/	oil	/zh/	azure
/oo/	moon	/ə/	above
/oo/	book		circus
/ôr/	fork	/ər/	bitter

A a

A·las·ka [ə·lăs′kə] The largest state of the United States, located in northwestern North America: Would you like to see the snowfields in *Alaska?*

Al·ba·ny [ôl′bə·nē] The capital city of New York: My cousin lives and works in *Albany,* New York.

al·read·y [ôl·rĕd′ē] Before or by a time mentioned earlier: We had *already* finished dinner when our friends arrived.

al·though [ôl·thō′] Even though: *Although* I studied for the test, I did not do well.

a·mount [ə·mount′] A quantity: The recipe calls for a small *amount* of butter.

anx·ious [ăngk′shəs] **anx·ious·ly** Worried; uneasy; eager: We waited *anxiously* for the plane to land.

314

arm-chair
[ärm′châr′] A
chair that has
arm supports:
Grandfather
loves to sit in the
arm-chair.

au·to·mo·bile
[ô′tə·mə·bēl′] A
four-wheeled
vehicle for
carrying people:
Watch out for
that *automobile*
as you cross the
street.

B b

be·neath [bǐ·nēth′] Under, directly
below: Put the chair *beneath* the
table.

be·side [bǐ·sīd′] At one side of:
Come and sit *beside* me.

bi·ceps [bī′sĕps] The large muscle
just above the elbow: The strong
man had large *biceps*.

bis·cuit [bǐs′kǐt]
bis·cuits A kind
of bread baked in
small cakes:
They made
biscuits for
dinner.

blind [blīnd] Unable to see: The
blind man depended on his cane to
help him cross the street.

blood [blŭd] The dark red liquid
that the heart pumps to the entire
body: The doctor told me that I did
not have enough iron in my *blood*.

both [bōth] The two together;
alike: *Both* girls like to swim.

bought [bôt] Past tense of *buy:* My
sister *bought* a new car.

boul·der [bōl′dər] A large rock or
stone that is not attached: The
boulder rolled down the side of the
mountain.

break·fast [brĕk′fəst] The first
meal of the day: Sara wanted to
get dressed before she ate her
breakfast.

brim [brǐm] A
rim that sticks
out, as on a hat:
He turned up the
brim of his hat.

brisk [brǐsk] Cool and refreshing:
The morning air was *brisk*.

buf·fa·lo
[bŭf′ə·lō] A wild
ox having a
thick body and
curved horns:
The Indians
hunted *buffalo*
for food and
clothing.

build [bĭld] To construct something: We will *build* a cabin near the lake.

bul·le·tin board [bŏŏl′ə·tən bôrd] A board on which notes or notices are hung: The store put the sale notices on the *bulletin board.*

bus·y [bĭz′ē] To be working or doing something: Mother was *busy* in the garden.

C c

cam·er·a [kăm′(ə)rə] A thing used to take pictures: We couldn't take pictures because we had no film for the *camera.*

camp·site [kămp′sīt] A place suitable for or used as the place where a tent is pitched for the night: We need to find a *campsite* with water before it gets dark.

cel·lo [chĕl′ō] A large, violin-like instrument with a deep tone. It is held between the musician's legs when played: The *cello* is an instrument in an orchestra.

cer·e·mo·ny [ser′ə·mō′nē] Any act or actions performed in a definite, set manner following certain rules or patterns: A king and queen are given their crowns in a *ceremony.*

chalk·stone [chôk′stōn] A kind of rock that is chalky in texture and suitable for carving or whittling: My brother is fond of carving *chalkstone.*

cheer·ful [chĭr′fəl] **cheer·ful·ly** Happy, joyous: She went on the errand *cheerfully.*

cher·ry blos·som [chĕr′ē blŏs′əm] **cher·ry blos·soms** The flower of a cherry tree: The *cherry blossoms* smell wonderful.

circle [sûr′kəl] A shape that is round: The children formed a *circle* to play dodge ball.

com·bi·na·tion [kŏm′bə·nā′shən] A group of people or things joined for a special purpose: I do not care for that *combination* of colors.

316

com·mit·tee [kə·mĭt′ē] A group of people chosen to do certain things: The council named a *committee* to study housing problems.

com·plain [kəm·plān] To find fault or say something is wrong: I have never heard him *complain* about anything.

con·di·tion [kən·dĭsh′ən]
con·di·tions The state of being of a person or thing: If the wind stays up we will have great sailing *conditions* for the races.

con·test [kŏn′tĕst] A game or competition: My friend won the book *contest*.

cot·ton·wood [kŏt′(ə)n·wo͞od] A tree having seeds covered with cottony tufts of hair: It sometimes looks like snow when the wind blows the *cottonwood* seeds around.

course [kôrs] **of course** Naturally; certainly: *Of course* she wanted to fly over her house on her first solo flight.

cup·board [kŭb′ərd] A cabinet with shelves used to store food or dishes: Put the clean plates on the first shelf in the *cupboard*.

D d

dan·de·li·on [dăn′də·lī′ən]
dan·de·li·ons A yellow flower that is considered a weed: We saw *dandelions* in the grass.

dan·ge·rous [dān′jər·əs] Likely to be unsafe: Climbing mountains can be a *dangerous* hobby.

dare [dâr] To have courage or to be bold: I wouldn't *dare* get home late.

daugh·ter [dô′tər] A female offspring: My uncle and aunt just had a baby *daughter*.

del·i·cate [dĕl′ə·kĭt] 1. Very fine in shape or design: The orchid is a *delicate* flower. 2. Easily broken or injured: The *delicate* glass dish was placed on the shelf.

de·sign [dĭ·zīn′] 1. A plan or sketch that is used as a pattern to make something. 2. To work out or draw plans or sketches: She will *design* a new house for me.

des·per·ate [dĕs′pər·ĭt] **des·per·ate·ly** Reckless because all hope seems gone: He was calling *desperately* for help.

des·sert [dĭ·zûrt′] Something sweet served at the end of a meal: We had fresh peaches and cookies for *dessert*.

de·ter·mine [dĭ·tûr′mĭn] **de·ter·mined** To firmly decide: The pupil was *determined* to do well on the test.

dis·guise [dĭs·gīz′] A costume that changes the way a person looks: He wore the *disguise* of a clown.

dis·miss [dĭs·mĭs′] **dis·missed** To tell or permit to leave: The teacher *dismissed* the class.

down·stairs [doun′stârz′] On or to a lower floor: Run *downstairs* and open the door, please.

E e

ed·i·tor [ĕd′ĭ·tər] A person who arranges, corrects, or prepares written material for publication: She is an *editor* for the local newspaper.

eight·y [ā′tē] The next number after seventy-nine: Grandma is *eighty* years old.

el·bow [ĕl′bō] The joint at the bend in the arm: I put my *elbow* on the table.

e·lev·en [ĭ·lĕv′ən] One more than ten: Bill will be *eleven* next Tuesday.

em·broi·der [ĭm·broi′dər] **em·broi·dered** To make designs in needlework: Flowers were *embroidered* on the collar of my dress.

en·er·gy [ĕn′ər·jē] Capacity for supplying power: *Energy* from steam can move a train.

Eng·land [ĭng′glənd] The largest island of Great Britain: Our mother was born in *England*.

e·nor·mous [ĭ·nôr′məs] Unusually large; immense: The cat looked *enormous* to the little mouse.

en·tire [ĭn·tīr′] All the parts of; the whole: We saw the *entire* game.

en·twine [ĭn·twīn′] To wrap or twist around: The rose bush will *entwine* the fence in several years.

en·ve·lope [ĕn′və·lōp] A flat paper case with a flap that folds over and seals, used for mailing letters: Put your return address in the upper left-hand corner of the *envelope*.

es·sen·tial [ə·sĕn′shəl] Very important or necessary: Food and water are *essential* to life.

ex·claim [ĭks·klām′] **ex·claimed** To cry out suddenly or speak with force, as in surprise: "That's great!" he *exclaimed*.

ex·pect [ĭk·spĕkt′] To be sure or almost sure of something: We *expect* to have a good time.

ex·pen·sive [ĭk·spĕn′sĭv] Costing a great deal: A fur coat is usually *expensive*.

ex·press [ĭk·sprĕs′] **ex·pressed** To say in words: He *expressed* how he felt about the accident.

F f

fa·mil·iar [fə·mĭl′yər] Well acquainted with or well known: She is *familiar* with me because I live next door.

fas·ten [făs′(ə)n] **fas·tened** To attach: She *fastened* the dog's leash to its collar.

fetch [fĕch] To go for, get, and bring back: Let's teach the dog to *fetch* the paper.

fierce [fîrs] Very cruel or violent: The *fierce* storm raged on through the night.

fi·nal [fī′nəl] **fi·nal·ly** At last: We *finally* got our mail.

fish·er·man [fĭsh′ər·mən] A person who catches fish for sport or work: The *fisherman* had a bucketful of trout.

flash·light [flăsh′līt′] A portable electric light that uses batteries: When the lights went out, we used a *flashlight* to help us see.

flat [flăt] **flats** The sign ♭ used in music to show that the note following is half a step lower than the normal tone: He did not like to play music with more than three *flats*.

for·ward [fôr′wərd] To move ahead: The parade moved *forward*.

full [fŏŏl] Filled as much as possible: The cup was *full* of water.

G g

gal·lop [găl′əp] **gal·loped** The fastest gait of a horse: The horse *galloped* across the plain.

ga·rage [gə·räzh′] A small building where cars are kept: Bob decided to clean out the *garage* on Saturday.

good·ness [gŏŏd′nĭs] A word used to express surprise: *Goodness*, I didn't expect you today!

gra·no·la [grə·nō′lə] A mixture of grains, cereals, and fruit which is eaten as a snack: Let's take *granola* with us on our hike.

green·house [grēn′ hous′] A heated building where plants are grown: The orchids are growing in the *greenhouse*.

gruff [grŭf] Harsh voice sounding unfriendly: The conductor's voice was *gruff* when calling out the train stops.

grump·y [grŭm′pē] Cranky or grouchy: The old man acted *grumpy*.

guard [gärd] **guards** A person or group who watches over or protects: Have you notified the *guards* about the theft?

guess [gĕs] To make a decision or give an answer without being sure: I had to *guess* at most of the answers.

guide [gīd] **guid·ed** To lead or show the way: The leader *guided* us through the museum.

gur·gle [gûr′gəl] **gur·gling** To flow with a bubbling sound: I could hear the *gurgling* stream outside my tent.

H h

half [hăf] Either of two equal parts: Jim shared *half* of his apple with Mike.

hap·pi·ness [hăp′ē·nĭs] Being pleased or happy: There was much *happiness* in our house when Mom came home from the hospital.

hey [hā] A cry used to attract attention or show surprise: "*Hey*! That hurts!" yelled Mark when the ball hit his head.

hoof [hoŏf *or* hoōf] **hooves** [hoŏvz *or* hoōvz] The feet of horses, cattle or other similar animals: Special iron shoes are used to protect horses' *hooves*.

howl [houl] **howled** Loud cries or sounds like cries: The wind *howled* all night.

I i

i·ci·cle [ī′sĭ·kəl] **i·ci·cles** A long piece of ice that hangs down: We had some *icicles* that were three feet long hanging from our roof.

im·ag·i·na·tion [ĭ·măj′ə·nā′shən] The power to form mental pictures; to see things in a new and creative way: An artist usually has a good *imagination*.

im·pa·tient [ĭm·pā′shənt] **im·pa·tient·ly** Not able to wait for something or someone without complaining: We waited *impatiently* for the bell to ring.

in·gre·di·ent [ĭn·grē′dē·ənt] **in·gre·di·ents** Something put into a mixture: I believe that salt and pepper are the missing *ingredients*.

in·spi·ra·tion [ĭn′spə·rā′shən] A good idea that comes to someone suddenly: The report on the need for exercise gave them the *inspiration* to go swimming.

J j

joy·ful [joi′fəl] Full of joy or happiness: The choir sang a *joyful* song.

L l

lad·der [lăd′ər] A device for climbing up and down: We needed to climb up a *ladder* to paint the ceiling.

las·so [lăs′ō] A long rope with a loop at one end used for catching cattle: A *lasso* is an important piece of equipment for a cowhand.

li·brar·y [lī′brer·ē *or* lī′brə·rē] A place where books are kept; a collection of books: We went to the *library* to get a book about horses.

lob·ster [lob′stər] A large tough-shelled animal with pincers that lives in the water: We caught a *lobster* and ate it for dinner.

lodge [lŏj] A small house or cabin in which a person may stay: We spent our vacation in the *lodge* by the lake.

long·horn [lông′hôrn′] A breed of cattle with long horns: There are few *longhorn* cattle where we live.

love·ly [lŭv′lē] Beautiful; enjoyable: It was a *lovely* day at the park.

M m

mac·in·tosh [măk′ən·täsh] A waterproof coat; raincoat: My grandfather gave me his *macintosh* to wear this winter.

mel·an·chol·y [mĕl′ən·kŏl′ē] Sad; very gloomy: We both seemed to be in a *melancholy* mood.

mel·o·dy [mĕl′ə·dē] **mel·o·dies** A tune; a group of musical tunes: The orchestra played the *melodies* of famous composers.

mis·sion [mĭsh′ən] A place where missionaries work and live: The doctor arrived at the *mission* in early June.

mix·ture [mĭks′chər] A combination of things blended together: There is a pleasing *mixture* of paintings and sculptures at the art gallery.

mud·dle [mŭd′(ə)l] **mud·dled** Confused or mixed up: The student driver became *muddled* during the driving test.

mur·mur [mûr′mər] **mur·mured** Making low, unclear, steady sounds: The jury *murmured* among themselves about the evidence.

mus·cle [mŭs′əl] **mus·cles** One of the fibrous tissues in the body that produces movement when contracted or stretched: Exercise will make our *muscles* strong.

mu·se·um [myōo·zē′əm] A place for keeping and displaying different kinds of collections: We went to the *museum* and saw the mummies of Egypt.

N n

nat·u·ral [năch′ər·əl] Not artificial, but already existing in nature: That is a *natural* lake.

nee·dle [nēd′(ə)l] A thin, steel rod with a hole in one end, used for sewing: The thread in the *needle* was a pretty shade of green.

New York [n(y)ōo yôrk] A state in the northern part of the United States: The Statue of Liberty is in *New York*.

nib·ble [nĭb′əl] **nib·bled** To bite or eat gently: The dog *nibbled* on the bone.

O o

oat·meal [ōt′mēl′] A cereal made from rolled oats: These are delicious *oatmeal* cookies.

o·bey [ō·bā′] To do as told: We should *obey* the traffic laws.

o·cean [ō′shən] A great body of salt water, as the Atlantic or Pacific: Much of the earth is covered not by land, but by *ocean*.

O·kla·ho·ma [ō′klə·hō′mə] A state in the southwestern part in the United States: A popular musical stage show was made about the state of *Oklahoma*.

om·e·let [ŏm′lĭt *or* ŏm′ə·lĭt] Eggs beaten together with milk or water and cooked by frying or baking: He makes a delicious ham and cheese *omelet*.

P p

pa [pä] Another name for dad or father: My father called his father *Pa*.

par·ka [pär·kə] A jacket with a hood: The *parka* will keep her warm.

pas·ture [păs′chər] Ground covered with grass and other plants for farm animals to eat: The cows are grazing in the *pasture*.

pa·ti·o [păt′ē·ō *or* pä′tē·ō] The paved area by the side of some houses: We had a barbeque picnic on the *patio*.

pet·ri·fy [pet′rə·fī] **pet·ri·fied** To become like stone: The *petrified* wood was used as a table.

pheas·ant [fĕz′ənt] A long-tailed bird that is often hunted for sport: The male *pheasant* has bright-colored feathers.

pine·ap·ple [pīn′ăp′əl] A large tropical fruit that is very juicy: We had *pineapple* for dessert.

Pitts·burgh [pĭts′bûrg′] A city in southwestern Pennsylvania: There are steel mills in *Pittsburgh*.

pleas·ure [plĕzh′ər] A feeling of enjoyment or delight: They listened with *pleasure* to the opera.

plop [plŏp] **plopped** To let the body fall heavily: Sam *plopped* into the soft armchair.

pom·pon [pŏm′pŏn] **pom·pons** The soft, white seed puff of a dandelion: The dandelion *pompons* covered the yard.

prac·tise [prăk′tĭs] **prac·tised** Variant spelling; To do over and over to gain greater skill: Baseball players must *practise* every day to play well.

prayer [prâr] A way of expressing thanks or worship: We gave a *prayer* of thanks for all we had received.

prom·ise [prŏm′ĭs] A statement made by a person to another person that a certain task will or will not be done: I *promise* to help clean the house.

proud [proud] **proud·ly** Having pride in what one does or has done: They *proudly* showed us their new home.

pro·vide [prə·vīd′] To supply or furnish: The teacher will *provide* a paper and pencil for you.

pur·pose [pûr′pəs] The reason for which a thing exists or is done; use: The *purpose* of a book cover is to keep a book clean.

R r

ra·di·o [rā′dē·ō] A device used to receive and send signals: Our *radio* went out before we could contact the Coast Guard.

rat·tle·snake [răt′(ə)l·snāk′] A poisonous snake with a tail that rattles when shaken: Watch out for the *rattlesnake*!

rec·i·pe [rĕs′ə·pē] A set of directions for cooking: May I have your *recipe* for the fruit salad?

red·wood [rĕd′wŏŏd′] A very tall evergreen tree that grows in northern California: The giant *redwood* trees are some of the oldest trees in the world.

re·la·tion [rĭ·lā′shən] **re·la·tions** Relatives, people in a family: All of our *relations* came for a family reunion.

re·mark·a·ble [rĭ·mär′kə·bəl] Worthy of notice; extraordinary: He made a *remarkable* recovery after the accident.

re·ply [rĭ·plī′] **re·plied** To give an answer or response: I *replied* immediately to the question.

re·port·er [rĭ·pôr′tər] A person who gives an account of a story, such as one employed by a newspaper: A *reporter* wrote the information about the department store fire.

re·quest [rĭ·kwĕst′] 1. To ask for: Did you *request* a copy of this book? 2. Something asked for: The library made a *request* for new books.

rhap·so·dy [răp′sə·dē] A piece of music not following set rules and full of strong feeling: She played a *rhapsody* on the piano.

ridge [rĭj] The line where two sloping surfaces meet: We hiked up to the mountain's *ridge*.

roar [rôr] **roar·ing** A loud noise or deep cry: The river sounded like a *roaring* cannon.

roost·er [rōōs′tər] A male chicken: Our *rooster* crows every morning.

ru·ral [rōōr′əl] Of or having to do with the country: They deliver our mail on a *rural* route.

S s

sad·ness [săd′nĭs] Being sorrowful; unhappiness: Her *sadness* showed in her eyes as she waved goodbye.

sand·wich [sănd′wĭch *or* săn′wĭch] Two slices of bread with meat or other filling between them: Would you like to have a peanut butter and jelly *sandwich* at the picnic?

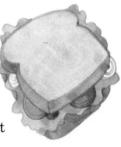

scene [sēn] A view of a place with everything in it: The painting of the country *scene* won an award.

sea gull [sē gŭl] A large gull or bird: A *sea gull* will follow a ship for scraps of food thrown overboard.

sev·en-thir·ty [sĕv′ən thûr′tē] Thirty minutes after the hour of seven o'clock.

sew [sō] **sew·ing** To mend by using a needle with thread: They are *sewing* their costumes for the party.

sha·dow [shăd′ō]
sha·dows An
image cast when
a person or thing
comes between a
light and
another surface:
My *shadow* runs
when I run.

sharp [shärp] **sharps** A sign ♯
placed in front of a written
musical note to show the note is
raised by half a tone: The black
keys on a piano are used to play
the *sharps*.

she'd [shēd] 1. Contraction for *she
had* or *she would:* She said *she'd*
see you tomorrow.

shep·herd·ess [shĕp′ərd·ĭs] A
woman who watches over sheep:
The *shepherdess* protected the
sheep from the wolf.

Sioux [sōō] A member of a group
of Indian tribes of the north
central United States: Have you
read this book about the *Sioux*
Indians?

skel·e·tal [skĕl′ə·təl] Having to do
with the skeleton, or bony
framework of the body: The x-ray
showed the *skeletal* area of her
leg.

smooth [smōōth] Without
roughness: The lake looked as
smooth as glass.

sol·emn [sŏl′əm] **sol·emn·ly**
Seriously or gravely: They
solemnly looked at the destroyed
house.

south·ern [sŭth′ərn] Toward the
south: We lived in the *southern*
part of the United States.

stam·pede [stăm·pēd′] A sudden
rush or flight caused by panic:
One frightened steer may start a
stampede.

state [stāt] A territory that, along
with other states, is part of the
federal government: Alaska
became a *state* in 1959.

stat·ue [stăch′ōō]
A likeness of a
person or animal
carved or molded
of a hard
material: The
statue of George
Washington was
in the park.

steer [stĭr] A male of beef cattle:
That *steer* is to be sold this week.

steer [stĭr] **steering** To direct the
course of a vehicle: We are
steering the boat toward the dock.

straw [strô] Dried stems or stalks of grasslike plants: Cows and horses eat *straw* in the winter.

stretch [strĕch] To extend: Sometimes I *stretch* when I first get out of bed.

stroll [strōl] A slow, easy walk: Let's take a *stroll* in the park.

stuff·y [stŭf′ē] Not well ventilated; not airy: The room was *stuffy*.

suede [swād] Soft leather that feels like velvet: My *suede* shoes got wet from the snow.

sup·ply [sə·plī′] **sup plies** Goods kept on hand: We had enough *supplies* to last a week.

swamp [swŏmp] An area of low, wet land: The *swamp* was drying up because of a lack of rainfall.

T t

tel·e·phone [tĕl′ə·fōn] A device for sending and receiving speech by electricity: My big brother Mike has his own *telephone*.

te·pee [tē′pē] A cone-shaped tent used as a home by some North American Indians: The chief's *tepee* was painted with bright pictures.

Tex·as [tĕk′səs] A large state in the southwestern United States: The people of *Texas* are proud of their state.

thief [thēf] **thieves** [thēvz] People who steal: The *thieves* stole the diamonds.

though [thō] As if: I feel as *though* I'd been there before.

ti·ger [tī′gər] **ti·gers** A large, yellow-and-black striped animal of the cat family: *Tigers* are found in the jungles of Asia.

ti·mid [tĭm′ĭd] **ti′·mid·ly** Fearful or shy: The dog walked *timidly* past the group of people.

tor·na·do
[tôr·nā′dō] A violent, destructive, whirling wind with a funnel-shaped cloud that moves along a path, sometimes touching the ground: The *tornado* tore up trees and blew the roof off the barn.

to·ward [tôrd *or* təwôrd′] To go near to or in the direction of: I moved *toward* the front of the room.

tri·ceps [trī′sĕps] A large muscle at the back of the arm that extends from the shoulder blade to the elbow: The *triceps* help you to stretch your arm.

twen·ty-five [twĕn′tē fīv] Five more than twenty: There are *twenty-five* pupils in our class.

U u

ugh [ŭg] A sound that is used to express the feeling of disgust or dislike: *Ugh!* That tastes awful!

un·com·fort·a·ble [ŭn·kŭm′fər·tə·bəl *or* ŭn·kŭmf′tə·bəl] Not having ease or satisfaction: That chair is *uncomfortable*.

un·fin·ished [ŭn·fĭn′ĭsht] Not completely done: The *unfinished* furniture needed to be painted.

un·pleas·ant [ŭn·plĕz′ənt] Not pleasing; disagreeable: The skunk had an *unpleasant* odor.

V v

val·ley [văl′ē] **val·leys** A low area between hills or mountains: Sheep and cattle grazed in the *valleys*.

val·u·a·ble [văl′y(o͞o)ə·bəl] Being worth money or effort: This picture is not very *valuable*, but it is my favorite.

W w

wa·ter·fall
[wô′tər·fôl′] Water falling from a high place: The *waterfall* splashed down into a clear river.

wa·ter·proof [wô′tər·pro͞of′ *or* wŏt′ər·pro͞of′] Allowing no water to get in: I was not wearing a *waterproof* watch when I went swimming.

wed·ding [wĕd′ĭng] The ceremony or celebration of a marriage: Their *wedding* will take place next Saturday.

whit·tle [(h)wĭt′(ə)l] **whit·tling** Cutting or shaving bits from wood: The boy cut his finger while he was *whittling*.

wig·gle [wig′əl] **wig·gled** To move from side to side; to squirm or twist: The dog *wiggled* its tail while waiting to be fed.

ACKNOWLEDGMENTS

For permission to adapt and reprint copyrighted materials, grateful acknowledgment is made to the following publishers, authors, and other copyright holders:

Atheneum Publishers, for "Foot Prints" in *See My Lovely Poison Ivy*. Text copyright ©1975 by Lilian Moore. Reprinted with the permission of Atheneum Publishers.

Curtis Publishing Company, for "Gift from Earth" by Kathleen Pacini from *Young World* magazine, copyright ©1975 by The Saturday Evening Post Company, Indianapolis, Indiana; for "The Mystery of Corbin Lodge" by Christine E. Scott from *Jack and Jill* magazine, copyright ©1968 by Curtis Publishing Company; and for "How I Got My Ten-Speed Bike" by John Griffith from *Jack and Jill* magazine, copyright ©1975 by The Saturday Evening Post Company, Indianapolis, Indiana, all adapted by permission of the publisher.

Elizabeth M. Graves, literary executor, for a condensation-adaptation of chapters 6-11 of *Grandma Moses: Favorite Painter* by Charles P. Graves. Copyright 1969 by Charles P. Graves. Published by Garrard Publishing Company. Adapted by permission of Elizabeth M. Graves.

Sibyl Hancock, author, for "Shingebis and the North Wind" from *Humpty Dumpty*, March 1972. Adapted by permission of the author.

Harcourt Brace Jovanovich, Inc., for "Gabrielle and Selena" by Peter Desbarats. Abridged and adapted from *Gabrielle and Selena* by Peter Desbarats. Copyright ©1968 by Peter Desbarats. By permission of Harcourt Brace Jovanovich, Inc.

Harper & Row, Publishers, Inc., for "Flat Stanley" adapted from *Flat Stanley* by Jeff Brown, pictures by Tomi Ungerer, text copyright ©1964 by Jeff Brown, pictures copyright ©1964 by Tomi Ungerer; for "Lengths of Time" from *Wonderful Time* by Phyllis McGinley (J. B. Lippincott Co.), copyright ©1965, 1966 by Phyllis McGinley; and for "Through Grandpa's Eyes" adapted from *Through Grandpa's Eyes* by Patricia MacLachlan, pictures by Deborah Ray, text copyright ©1979 by Patricia MacLachlan, illustrations copyright ©1980 by Ray Studios, Inc., all by permission of Harper & Row, Publishers, Inc.

E. P. Dutton and Co., Inc., for "The House at Pooh Corner" from *The House at Pooh Corner* by A. A. Milne, illustrated by Ernest H. Shepard, copyright ©1928 by E. P. Dutton and Co., Inc., renewed 1956 by A. A. Milne, reprinted by permission of the publisher; for "Do You Have the Time, Lydia?" from *Do You Have the Time, Lydia?* by Evaline Ness, copyright ©1971 by Evaline Ness, reprinted by permission of the publisher, E. P. Dutton, Inc.; and for "The Flower-fed Buffaloes" from *Going-to-the-Stars* by Vachel Lindsay, copyright 1926 by D. Appleton & Co., renewed 1954 by Elizabeth C. Lindsay, reprinted by permission of E. P. Dutton, Inc.

Four Winds Press, a division of Scholastic, Inc., for "Cunningham's Rooster" adapted from *Cunningham's Rooster* by Barbara Brenner. Text copyright ©1975 by Barbara Brenner. Reprinted by permission of Four Winds Press, a division of Scholastic, Inc.

Garrard Publishing Company, for "Pecos Bill Rides a Tornado" from *Pecos Bill Rides a Tornado* by Wyatt Blassingame, reprinted with the permission of Garrard Publishing Company, Champaign, IL 61820.